CHARLES DARWIN

THE ORIGIN OF SPECIES
by Means of Natural Selection,
or the Preservation of Favoured Races
in the Struggle for Life

Edited and Abridged
By
CHARLOTTE and WILLIAM IRVINE

FREDERICK UNGAR PUBLISHING CO.
NEW YORK

MILESTONES
OF THOUGHT
in the History of Ideas

Edited by
F. W. STROTHMANN
Stanford University

Second Printing, 1957

Copyright 1956 by
Frederick Ungar Publishing Co.

Printed in the United States of America

Library of Congress Catalog Card Number: 56-7502

CHARLES DARWIN
1809-1882

DESCENDED from a nationally famous grandfather and a locally famous father—both formidable in stature, voice, and authoritative fluency—Charles Darwin grew up as a rather unimpressive young man with a passion for beetle collecting and snipe shooting, and an apologetic sense that he ought to be doing something more important. He began to study for the family profession of medicine at the University of Edinburgh, but finding himself too squeamish for the horrors of early nineteenth-century surgery, turned once more to the pleasure of snipe shooting and an ample income. With thunders of despair, his father proposed he study for the ministry at Cambridge. Charles consulted a sensitive but docilely orthodox conscience and agreed.

At Cambridge theology was so rational and secular that it was an excellent preparation for science. And even as he studied theology, beetle collecting led Charles, by a very devious and very English process of following his nose, into biology and geology. In 1831 his botany professor, J. S. Henslow, recommended him for the post of naturalist on the *H. M. S. Beagle*, a tiny, 24-ton brig which was to make a five-year voyage surveying the coast of South American. The consent of his father was obtained, and Charles sailed. He discovered modern geology in the first volume of Lyell's *Principles*, and rediscovered it on the peaks of the Andes and the plains of Argentina. Evolution was then a discreditable heresy to which respectable scientists tried to close their minds. Charles tried conscientiously to close his mind, but certain facts about South American flora and fauna haunted him like ghosts. Secretly, guiltily—while his Christian faith slowly evaporated away—he took up the problem of the origin of species.

Darwin returned to England; married his cousin Emma Wedgwood; published famous books on his travels, barnacles, and geology; collected more facts on evolution; perfected his theory of natural selection; wrote preliminary sketches—but put off publication year after year, unwilling to advocate a disreputable theory without at the same time being able to prove it. For though no man has affected them more profoundly, Charles Darwin was like many Englishmen always a little suspicious of ideas. Finally, in 1858, he received from A. R. Wallace in Maylaya a scientific paper which exploded like a bombshell on his quiet world of anxious industry. Lying ill with malaria in a tropical jungle, Wallace had sketched out in a single week the theory which Darwin had taken twenty years to elaborate. At the repeated urging of friends, Darwin finally wrote a brief paper similar to Wallace's, and both papers were read before the Linnean Society. They were received in grave and somewhat stunned silence. Darwin now wrote a further summary of his ideas, which as usual grew into a long book. *The Origin of Species* appeared in 1859.

So many facts, so ingeniously and cautiously explained, could not possibly be received with calm, even by the calmest scientists. In fact, they produced over Europe and America intellectual hurricanes, earthquakes, avalanches, and deluges which lasted for more than a decade. Darwin was astonished. Still, he had planned a shrewd, far-sighted campaign for the acceptance of his book; and working as a charming and accomplished diplomatist behind the scenes, and enjoying before the world the aid of such men as Thomas Huxley in England, Asa Gray in the United States, and Ernst Haeckel in Germany, he found himself by 1870 the acknowledged pontiff of an *ism* and one of the most famous men in the world. Evolution was accepted as a fact and natural selection almost universally preferred as its explanation. Zoology, botany, and anthropology were revolutionized. Ethics, religion, philosophy, indeed, every field of thought, were radically altered.

Darwin's second most important work was *The Descent of Man,* which appeared in 1871. Thereafter, he did what he wanted. That is, he gave up all amusements and devoted himself to his favorite kinds of hard work. As much as possible, he abandoned his study and his desk for his garden and his hothouse, living more and more among facts and flowers and less and less among ideas and words, for writing caused him even more trouble and anxiety than thinking did. Having received many honors, including an L.L.D. degree from his own Cambridge University, he died of a heart attack in 1882 and was buried close by Sir Isaac Newton in Westminster Abbey.

SELECTED BIBLIOGRAPHY

Darwin, Charles. *Journal of Researches into the Natural History and Geology of the countries visited during the Voyage of H.M.S. Beagle Round the World, under The Command of Capt. Fitz Roy, R.N.* Authorized Edition. New York: D. Appleton and Company, 1896.

——— *The Origin of Species By Means of Natural Selection or the Preservation of Favored Races in the Struggle for Life, and The Descent of Man and Selection in Relation to Sex.* The Modern Library. New York: Random House.

Darwin, Francis, editor. *The Life and Letters of Charles Darwin, Including an Autobiographical Chapter.* Authorized Edition. New York: D. Appleton and Company, 1896. (Includes Darwin's *Autobiography* and a chapter by T. H. Huxley on the reception of the *Origin of Species.*)

Dunn, L. C., and Dobzhansky, Th. *Heredity, Race, and Society.* A Mentor Book. New York: The New American Library, 1946.

Huxley, Julian, and Fisher, James. *The Living Thoughts of Darwin.* The Living Thoughts Library. New York: Longmans, Green and Company, 1939.

Huxley, Thomas H. *Evolution and Ethics and Other Essays.* Authorized Edition. New York: D. Appleton and Company, 1897.

Irvine, William. *Apes, Angels, and Victorians, The Story of Darwin, Huxley, and Evolution.* New York: McGraw-Hill Book Company, 1955.

Simpson, George Gaylord. *The Meaning of Evolution, A Study of the History of Life and of Its Significance for Man.* A special revised and abridged edition. Mentor, No. M66.

NOTE

This little book is an abridgment of the sixth (1872) edition, which embodies Darwin's final revisions and corrections.

In reducing *The Origin of Species* to approximately one-seventh of its length, the editors have attempted to cut out words rather than ideas or facts. They have eliminated many repetitions, summaries, expostulations with Victorian "prejudice," citations of authority, and—inevitably—some illustrations or applications of general principles. They have simplified punctuation, frequently re-paragraphed, and—once or twice—transposed paragraphs. Only rarely have they changed the order or the phrasing of Darwin's sentences. They have omitted his "Historical Sketch" and "Introduction." The text is essentially what he wrote.

CONTENTS

CHAPTER I

Variation under Domestication

Conditions of life produce, directly or indirectly, changes which are either definite or indefinite

No case is on record of a variable organism ceasing to vary under cultivation. Our oldest cultivated plants, such as wheat, still yield new varieties: our oldest domesticated animals are still capable of rapid improvement or modification.

The conditions of life appear to act in two ways—directly on the organisation or indirectly by affecting the reproductive system. With respect to the direct action, there are two factors: the nature of the organism and the nature of the conditions. The former seems to be much more important; for similar variations sometimes arise under dissimilar conditions, and dissimilar variations arise under conditions nearly uniform. The effects on the offspring may be considered as definite when all or nearly all the offspring of individuals exposed to certain conditions during several generations are modified in the same manner. There can be little doubt about many slight changes—such as size from the amount of food, colour from the nature of the food, thickness of the skin and hair from climate, etc. Such facts as the extraordinary outgrowths which variably follow from the insertion of a drop of poison by a gall-producing insect show what singular modifications might result in plants from a chemical change in the sap.

Indefinite variability is much more common than definite, and more important in the formation of our domestic races. We see it in the endless slight peculiarities which distinguish the individuals of the same species, and which cannot be accounted for by inheritance. Even strongly marked differences occasionally appear in the young of the same litter and in seedlings from the same seed-capsule. At long intervals of time monstrosities arise; but monstrosities cannot be separated by any distinct line from slighter variations. All such changes of structure may be considered as the indefinite effects of the conditions of life on each individual organism, in nearly the way the chill affects different men in an indefinite manner, according to their constitution, causing coughs or colds, rheumatism, or inflammation of various organs.

The reproductive system is extremely sensitive to surrounding conditions

With respect to the indirect action of changed conditions, namely, through the reproductive system being affected, variability is induced, partly from this system being extremely sensitive to change, and partly from causes to be discussed later. Many facts clearly show how susceptible the reproductive system is to slight changes in the surrounding conditions. Nothing is more easy than to tame an animal, and few things more difficult than to get it to breed freely under confinement, even when the male and female unite. In some cases a trifling change, such as a little more or less water at some particular period of growth, will determine whether or not a plant will produce seeds. When we see domesticated animals and plants, though sickly, breeding freely under confinement; and when, on the other hand, we see individuals, though taken young from a state of nature perfectly tamed and healthy, yet having their reproductive system so seriously affected as to fail to act, we need not be surprised at this system, when it does act under confinement, acting irregularly, and producing offspring somewhat unlike their parents. I may add, that as some organisms breed freely under the most unnatural conditions, showing that their reproductive organs are not easily affected; so will some animals and plants withstand domestication or cultivation, and vary hardly more than in a state of nature.

Many changes are inherited, and many very distinct domestic races have developed from one or more wild species   Changed habits produce an inherited effect, as in the period of the flowering of plants when transported from one climate to another. With animals the increased use or disuse of parts has had a more marked influence; thus in the domestic duck the bones of the wing weigh less and the bones of the leg more than do the same bones in the wild-duck.

Many laws regulate variation. I will here only allude to correlated variation. Some instances of correlation are quite whimsical; thus entirely white, blue-eyed cats are generally deaf. White sheep and pigs are injured by certain plants, whilst dark-coloured individuals escape. Hairless dogs have imperfect teeth. Hence if man goes on selecting and thus augmenting any peculiarity, he will almost certainly modify unintentionally other parts of the structure, owing to the laws of correlation.

Any variation not inherited is unimportant for us. When any rare deviation appears in the parent—say, once amongst several million individuals—and reappears in the child, the doctrine of chances almost compels us to attribute its reappearance to inheritance. Every one must have heard of cases of albinism, hairy bodies, etc., appearing in several members of the same family. If strange and rare deviations are inherited, commoner deviations may be freely admitted to be inheritable. Perhaps the correct way of viewing the subject would be to look at the inheritance of every character as the rule, and non-inheritance as the anomaly.

The laws governing inheritance are for the most part unknown. No one can say why the child often reverts in certain characters to its grandfather or grandmother or more remote ancestor, why a peculiarity is often trans-

mitted from one sex to both sexes or to one sex alone.
Though there is no apparent reason why a peculiarity
should appear at any particular age, yet it does tend to
appear in the offspring at the same period at which it first
appeared in the parent. I believe this rule to be of the
highest importance in explaining the laws of embryology.

Domestic races are less uniform than true species,
and often have a somewhat monstrous character, differing in extreme degree in some one part compared with the
nearest allied species. With these exceptions domestic
races of the same species differ from each other in the same
manner as do species of the same genus in nature, though
in lesser degree. This must be true, for many domestic
races have been ranked by some competent judges as
descendants of aboriginally distinct species, and by other
competent judges as mere varieties. If any well marked
distinction existed between a domestic race and a species,
this doubt would not so perpetually recur. If, for instance, it could be shown that the greyhound, bloodhound,
terrier, and bull-dog were the offspring of any single
species, such facts would make us doubt the immutability
of the many closely allied natural species—for instance,
of the many foxes—inhabiting different quarters of the
world. I believe that a small part of the difference in
dogs is due to their being descended from distinct species.
In the case of strongly marked races of some other domesticated species, there is strong evidence that all are descended from a single wild stock. I am inclined to believe,
in opposition to several authors, that all the races of
horses belong to the same species. Having kept nearly
all the English breeds of the fowl alive, having bred and
crossed them, and examined their skeletons, it appears to
me almost certain that all are the descendants of the wild
Indian fowl, Gallus bankiva. The evidence is clear that
ducks and rabbits are all descended from the common wild
duck and rabbit.

The fact that the numerous breeds of pigeons are more diverse than many distinct natural species, and all descend from one single species, poses a fundamental question

Believing that it is best to study some special group, I have, after deliberation, taken up domestic pigeons. I have kept every breed which I could obtain, and have been most kindly favoured with skins from several quarters of the world. Many treatises in different languages have been published on pigeons, some of them being of considerable antiquity. I have associated with several eminent fanciers, and have been permitted to join two London Pigeon Clubs. The diversity of the breeds is something astonishing. The common tumbler has the singular inherited habit of flying at great height in a compact flock, and tumbling in the air head over heels. The pouter has a much elongated body, and its enormously developed crop, which it glories in inflating, excites astonishment and even laughter. The turbit has the habit of continually expanding, slightly, the upper part of the oesophagus. The trumpeter and laugher, as their names express, utter a very different coo from the other breeds. The fantail has thirty or even forty tail-feathers. Several other less distinct breeds might be specified.

The skeletons of the breeds differ. The vertebrae vary in number, as does the number of ribs. The period at which the perfect plumage is acquired varies, as does the down of newly hatched birds. Shape and size of the eggs, manner of flight, voice, and disposition differ remarkably. If he were told they were wild birds, I do not believe any ornithologist would place the English carrier, the short-faced tumbler, the runt, the barb, pouter, and fantail in the same genus; especially as in each breed sub-breeds, or species, as he would call them, could be shown him. Great as are the differences, I am fully convinced that the common opinion of naturalists is correct, that all are descended from the rock-pigeon, including its sub-species, which differ in trifling respects.

The rock-pigeon is of a slaty blue with white loins. The tail has a dark bar, with the outer feathers edged with white. The wings have two black bars. These several marks do not occur together in any other species of the whole family. Now, in every one of the domestic breeds, taking thoroughly well-bred birds, all the above marks sometimes concur perfectly developed. Moreover, when birds belonging to distinct breeds are crossed, none of which are blue or have any of the above-specified marks, the mongrel offspring are very apt suddenly to acquire these characters. To give one instance:—I crossed some white fantails, which breed very true, with some black barbs—and blue varieties of barbs are so rare that I never heard of an instance in England; the mongrels were black, brown and mottled. I also crossed a barb with a spot, which is a white bird with a red tail and red spot on the forehead, and which notoriously breeds very true; the mongrels were dusky and mottled. I then crossed a mongrel barb-fantail with a mongrel barb-spot, and they produced a bird of as beautiful a blue colour, with white loins, double black wing-bar, and barred and white-edged tail-feathers, as any wild rock-pigeon! We can understand these facts, on the principle of reversion to ancestral characters, if all the domestic breeds are descended from the rock-pigeon, for when there has been no cross, and there is a tendency in the breed to revert to a character which was lost during some former generation, this tendency may be transmitted undiminished for an indefinite number of generations.

Lastly, the hybrids or mongrels from all the breeds of pigeon are perfectly fertile. Now, hardly any cases have been ascertained with certainty of hybrids from two distinct species of animals being perfectly fertile. To suppose that species, aboriginally as distinct as carriers, tumblers, pouters, and fantails are now, should yield off-spring perfectly fertile *inter se,* would be rash in the extreme. From these and other equally valid reasons, we may conclude that all our domestic breeds are descended from the rock-pigeon with its geographical sub-species.

I have never met a pigeon, or poultry, or duck, or rabbit fancier, who was not convinced that each main breed was descended from a distinct species. Though they well know that each race varies slightly, for they win their prizes by selecting slight differences, yet they ignore all general arguments, and refuse to sum up in their minds slight differences accumulated during many generations. May not naturalists knowing far less of inheritance than does the breeder, learn a lesson of caution, when they deride the idea of species in a state of nature being lineal descendants of other species?

By selection, through "accumulative change," man has actually produced an astounding number of new species

A remarkable feature in our domesticated races is that we see in them adaptation, not to their own good, but to man's use or fancy. Some useful variations have probably arisen suddenly, or by one step. But we must look further than to mere variability. The key is man's power of accumulative selection: nature gives successive variations; man adds them up in certain directions. In this sense he may be said to have made for himself useful breeds.

Several eminent breeders have, within a single lifetime, modified largely their breeds of cattle. Lord Somerville, speaking of what breeders have done for sheep says: "It would seem as if they had chalked out upon a wall a form perfect in itself, and then had given it existence." The importance of selection consists in the great effect produced by the accumulation in one direction, of differences absolutely inappreciable by an uneducated eye—differences which I for one have vainly attempted to appreciate. Not one man in a thousand has the accuracy of eye and judgment to become an eminent breeder.

The same principles are followed by horticulturists; but the variations are here more abrupt. With plants, there is another means of observing the accumulated effects of selection—namely, the diversity of whatever part is valued, in comparison with the leaves and flowers of the same set of varieties. How much the fruit of the different kinds of goose-berries differ and yet the flowers present very slight differences. The continued selection of slight variations, either in the leaves, the flowers, or the fruit, will produce races differing from each other chiefly in these characters.

The principle of selection is no modern discovery. In rude and barbarous periods of English history choice animals were often imported, and laws passed to prevent their exportation: the destruction of horses under a certain size was ordered. The principle of selection I find distinctly given in an ancient Chinese encyclopaedia. Explicit rules are laid down by some of the Roman classical writers. Savages now sometimes cross their dogs with canine wild animals, to improve the breed. Livingstone states that good domestic breeds are highly valued by the negroes in the interior of Africa who have not associated with Europeans. It would, indeed, have been strange had attention not been paid to breeding, for the inheritance of good and bad qualities is so obvious.

Eminent breeders select with a distinct object in view. For our purpose, a form of Selection, which may be called Unconscious, is more important. Thus, a man who intends keeping pointers naturally breeds from his own best dogs, but he has no wish or expectation of permanently altering the breed. Nevertheless, this process, continued during centuries, would improve and modify any breed. Youatt gives an excellent illustration of the effects of a course of unconscious selection: The two flocks of Leicester sheep kept by Mr. Buckley and Mr. Burgess, "have been purely bred from the original stock of Mr. Bakewell for upwards of fifty years. There is not a suspicion that the owner of either of them has deviated from the pure blood of Mr. Bakewell's flock, and yet the difference between the sheep of these two gentlemen is so great that they have the appearance of being quite different varieties."

Among savages, any one animal particularly useful to them would be carefully preserved during famines and other accidents, to which savages are so liable, and such choice animals would thus generally leave more offspring than the inferior ones; so that there would be a kind of unconscious selection going on.

In plants the same gradual process of improvement, through occasional preservation of the best individuals, may be recognized in the increased size and beauty of the rose, dahlia, and other plants, when compared with older varieties. No one would expect to get a first-rate dahlia from the seed of a wild plant. A large amount of change, unconsciously accumulated, explains the fact that in a number of cases we do not know the wild parent-stocks of the plants which have been longest cultivated in our flower and kitchen gardens. If it has taken centuries or thousands of years to modify most of our plants up to their present standard of usefulness, we can understand how it is that neither Australia, the Cape of Good Hope, nor any other region inhabited by quite uncivilized man, has afforded us a single plant worth culture.

Domestic animals kept by uncivilized man almost always have to struggle for their own food, at least during certain seasons. And in two countries very differently circumstanced, individuals of the same species, having slightly different constitutions or structure, would often succeed better in one country than in the other; and thus by a process of "natural selection," two sub-breeds might be formed. This, perhaps, partly explains why the varieties kept by savages have more of the character of true species than the varieties kept in civilized countries.

On the view here given, we can, I think, understand differences in our domestic races being so great in external characters, and relatively so slight internally. Man can select only with much difficulty any deviation which is not visible, and rarely cares for what is internal. He can never act by selection, excepting on variations first given him in some slight degree by nature. The man who first selected a pigeon with a slightly larger tail never dreamed that its descendants would become fantails through long-continued, partly unconscious and partly methodical, selection.

We know hardly anything about the origin of any domestic breeds. A man breeds from an individual with some slight deviation or takes care in matching his best animals, and the improved animals slowly spread in the immediate neighborhood. When further improved, they will spread more widely and be recognized as something distinct and valuable. They will then probably first receive a provincial name. As soon as the points of value are once acknowledged, the principle of unconscious selection will always tend slowly to add to the characteristic features of the breed. But the chance will be infinitely small of any record having been preserved of such slow, varying, and insensible changes.

I will now say a few words on the circumstances favourable to man's power of selection. A high degree of variability is obviously favourable, as freely giving the materials for selection to work on. The chance of variations manifestly useful or pleasing to man will be much increased by a large number of individuals being kept. Hence, number is of the highest importance. Nurserymen, from keeping large stocks of the same plant, are generally far more successful than amateurs in raising varieties. The animal or plant should be so highly valued that the closest attention is paid to the slightest deviations. I have seen it gravely remarked, that it was most fortunate that the strawberry began to vary just when gardeners began to attend to this plant.

With animals, facility in preventing crosses is important. Wandering savages or the inhabitants of open plains rarely possess more than one breed of the same species. Cats, from their nocturnal rambling habits, cannot be easily matched, and, although so much valued by women and children, we rarely see a distinct breed long kept up; such breeds as we do sometimes see are almost always imported.

Some authors have maintained that the amount of variation in our domestic productions is soon reached, and can never be afterwards exceeded. It would be rash to assert that the limit has been attained in any one case; or that characters could not, after remaining fixed for many centuries, again vary under new conditions of life. No doubt, as Mr. Wallace has remarked with much truth, a limit will be at last reached. For instance, there must be a limit to the fleetness of any terrestrial animal. But what concerns us is that the domestic varieties of the same species differ from each other in almost every character, which man has attended to and selected, more than do the distinct species of the same genera.

CHAPTER II

Variation under Nature

No one definition of species has satisfied all naturalists. Generally the term includes the unknown element of a distinct act of creation. In the term "variety" community of descent is almost universally implied, though it can rarely be proved. We have also what are called monstrosities; but they graduate into varieties.

It may be doubted whether sudden and considerable deviations of structure are ever permanently propagated in a state of nature. Almost every part of every organic being is so beautifully related to its complex conditions of life that it seems as improbable that any part should have been suddenly produced perfect, as that complex machines should have been invented by man in a perfect state. Under domestication monstrosities sometimes occur which resemble normal structures in widely different animals. But I have failed yet to find, after diligent search, cases of monstrosities resembling normal structures in nearly allied forms, and these alone bear on the question. If monstrous forms of this kind ever do appear in a state of nature and are capable of reproduction (which is not always the case), as they occur rarely and singly, their preservation would depend on unusually favourable circumstances. They would also during the first and succeeding generations cross with the ordinary form, and thus their abnormal character would almost inevitably be lost.

The many slight differences which appear in the offspring from the same parents may be called individual differences. These are of the highest importance for us, for they are often inherited, and thus afford materials for natural selection to act on and accumulate, in the same manner as man accumulates individual differences in his domesticated productions. These individual differences generally affect what naturalists consider unimportant parts, but I am convinced that the most experienced naturalist would be surprised at the number of cases of variability, even in important parts of structure, which he could collect on good authority, as I have collected, during a course of years. It should be remembered that systematists are far from being pleased at finding variability in important characters, and that there are not many men who will laboriously examine internal and important organs, and compare them in many specimens of the same species. Authors sometimes argue in a circle when they state that important organs never vary; for they rank those parts as important (as some naturalists have honestly confessed) which do not vary.

Individuals of the same species often present great differences of structure, independently of variation, as in the two sexes of various animals, in the two or three castes of sterile females or workers among insects, and in the larval states of many of the lower animals. There are, also, cases of dimorphism and trimorphism. Mr. Wallace has shown that the females of certain species of butterflies regularly appear under two or even three conspicuously distinct forms. Although in most of these cases, the two or three forms, both with animals and plants, are not now connected by intermediate gradations, it is probable that they were once thus connected.

Competent naturalists disagree in ranking many closely allied forms

The forms which possess the character of species but which are so closely similar to other forms or so closely linked to them by intermediate gradations that naturalists do not like to rank them as distinct species, are in several respects the most important for us. Practically, when a naturalist can unite by means of intermediate links any two forms, he treats the one as a variety of the other. In very many cases, however, one form is ranked as a variety, not because the intermediate links have actually been found, but because analogy leads the observer to suppose either that they do now somewhere exist or may formerly have existed; and here a wide door for the entry of doubt and conjecture is opened. Hence, the opinion of naturalists having sound judgment and wide experience seems the only guide. We must, however, decide by a majority of naturalists, for few well-marked and well-known varieties can be named which have not been ranked as species by at least some competent judges. Amongst animals which unite for each birth, and which are highly locomotive, doubtful forms can rarely be found within the same country, but are common in separated areas. How many of the birds and insects in North America and Europe which differ slightly have been ranked by one eminent naturalist as undoubted species, and by another as varieties, or as they are often called, geographical races.

Many years ago, when comparing, and seeing others compare, the birds from the closely neighboring islands of the Galapagos archipelago, one with another, and with those from the American mainland, I was much struck how entirely vague and arbitrary is the distinction between species and varieties. A wide distance between the homes of two doubtful forms leads many naturalists to rank them as distinct species; but what distance will suffice? If that between America and Europe is ample, will that between Europe and the Azores, or between the several islets of these small archipelagos, be sufficient?

I may here allude to a remarkable memoir lately published by A. de Candolle, on the oaks of the whole world. No one ever had more ample materials or could have

worked on them with more zeal and sagacity. He speci-
fies above a dozen characters which may be found varying
even on the same branch, sometimes without any assign-
able reason. He gives the rank of species to the forms that
differ by characters never varying on the same tree, and
never found connected by intermediate states. He also
adds that it is the best known species which present the
greatest number of varieties. Finally, de Candolle admits
that out of 300 species, at least two-thirds are provisional,
that is, are not known strictly to fulfill the definition above
given. De Candolle no longer believes that species are
immutable creations, but concludes that the derivative
theory is the most natural one, "and the most accordant
with the known facts in palaeontology, geographical botany and zoology, of anatomical structure and classification."

Certainly no clear line of demarcation has as yet been
drawn between species and sub-species. Differences blend
into each other by an insensible series.

Natural selection creates in-
cipient varieties from the raw
material of individual differ-
ences; classifications merely
denote accumulated degrees
of difference

Hence I look at individual
differences, though of
small interest to the systematist, as of the highest
importance for us, as being
the first steps towards
such slight varieties as are
barely thought worth recording in works on natural history. And I look at varieties which are in any degree
more distinct and permanent, as steps towards permanent
varieties; and at the latter, as leading to sub-species, and
then to species. With respect to the more important and
adaptive characters, the passage from one stage of difference to another, may be safely attributed to the cumulative
action of natural selection, and to the effects of the increased use or disuse of parts. A well-marked variety may
therefore be called an incipient species; but whether this
belief is justifiable must be judged by the weight of the

various facts and considerations to be given throughout this work.

Not all varieties or incipient species attain the rank of species. If a variety were to flourish so as to exceed in numbers the parent species, it would then rank as the species, and the species as the variety; or it might come to supplant and exterminate the parent species; or both might co-exist, and both rank as independent species.

From these remarks it will be seen that I look at the term species as one arbitrarily given, for the sake of convenience, to a set of individuals closely resembling each other, and that it does not essentially differ from the term variety, which is given to less distinct and more fluctuating forms. The term variety, again, in comparison with mere individual differences, is also applied arbitrarily, for convenience' sake.

Dominant species vary most, producing varieties equipped by inheritance to flourish and become incipient species

Wide-ranging, much diffused, and common species vary most. I thought that some interesting results might be obtained in regard to species which vary most, by tabulating all the varieties in several well-worked floras. Alphone de Candolle and others have shown that plants which have very wide ranges generally present varieties; they are exposed to diverse physical conditions and they come into competition (an equally or more important circumstance) with different sets of organic beings. But my tables further show that, in any limited country, the species which abound most in individuals, and the species which are most widely diffused within their own country oftenest give rise to varieties sufficiently well-marked to have been recorded in botanical works. Hence it is the most flourishing dominant species which oftenest produce well-marked varieties, or, as I consider them, incipient species. As varieties necessarily have to struggle with the other inhabitants of the country, the species which are already dominant will be the most likely to yield offspring, which, though in some slight degree modified, still inherit those advantages that enabled their parents to become dominant over their compatriots. In these remarks on predominance, reference is made only to the forms which come into competition with each other, and more especially to the members of the same genus or class having nearly similar habits of life. One of the higher plants is not the less dominant because some parasitic fungus is infinitely more numerous in individuals, and more widely diffused. But if a parasitic fungus exceeds its allies in the above respects, it will then be dominant within its own class.

If the plants inhabiting a country be divided into two equal masses, all those in the larger genera (i.e., those including many species) being placed on one side, and the smaller on the other side, the former will be found to include a somewhat larger number of the very common and much diffused or dominant species. Moreover, the species of the large genera present a larger number of varieties. These facts are of plain signification on the view that species are only strongly-marked and permanent varieties; for where the manufactory of species has been active, we ought generally to find the manufactory still in action. And this certainly holds true, if varieties be looked at as incipient species. It is not that all large genera are now varying much, or that no small genera are now varying and increasing. All that we want to show is, that, where many species of a genus have been formed, on an average many are still forming; and this certainly holds good.

Species of a genus are related to each other as are varieties of a species: the fact is explicable only on the theory of cumulative differentiation

In large genera the amount of difference between the species is often exceedingly small. No naturalist pretends that all the species of a genus are equally distinct from each other. Little groups of species are generally clustered like satellites around other species. And what are varieties but groups of forms, unequally related to each other, and clustered round their parent-species? Undoubtedly the amount of difference between varieties, is much less than that between species. But we shall see how the lesser difference between varieties tends to increase into the greater difference between species. Species very closely allied to other species apparently have restricted ranges. In many respects the species of large genera present a strong analogy with varieties. And we can clearly understand these analogies, if species once existed as varieties; whereas, these analogies are utterly inexplicable if species are independent creations.

CHAPTER III

Struggle for Existence

A struggle for existence in-
evitably results from the rap-
idity with which all beings
naturally multiply

How do varieties, species,
and genera originate?
From the struggle for life.
Owing to this struggle,
variations, if they be in
any degree profitable to individuals, will tend to the
preservation of such individuals, and will generally be
inherited by the offspring. The offspring, also, will thus
have a better chance of surviving, for, of the many individuals born, but a small number can survive. I have
called this principle, by which each slight variation, if
useful, is preserved, Natural Selection, in order to mark
its relation to man's power of selection. But the expres-
sion often used by Mr. Herbert Spencer of the Survival
of the Fittest is more accurate, and is sometimes equally
convenient.

Nothing is easier than to admit in words the truth of
the universal struggle for life, or more difficult constantly
to bear in mind. We behold the face of nature bright
with gladness, we often see superabundance of food; we
do not see or we forget, that the birds which are idly singing round us mostly live on insects or seeds, and are thus
constantly destroying life; or we forget how largely these
songsters, or their eggs, or their nestlings, are destroyed
by birds and beasts of prey.

I use the term struggle for existence in a large and
metaphorical sense including not only the life of the individual, but success in leaving progeny. A plant which

annually produces a thousand seeds, of which only one of an average comes to maturity, may be said to struggle with the plants which already clothe the ground. The mistletoe is dependent on a few trees, but can only in a farfetched sense be said to struggle with them, for, if too many of these parasites grow on the same tree, it languishes and dies. But seedling mistletoes, growing close together on the same branch, may be said to struggle with each other. As the mistletoe is disseminated by birds, its existence depends on them; and it may be said to struggle with other fruit-bearing plants, in tempting the birds to devour and thus disseminate its seeds. In these several senses, which pass into each other, I use for convenience' sake the general term of Struggle for Existence.

As more individuals are produced than can possibly survive, there must in every case be a struggle for existence, either one individual with another of the same species, or with those of distinct species, or with the physical conditions of life. It is the doctrine of Malthus applied with manifold force to the whole animal and vegetable kingdoms; for in this case there can be no artificial increase of food, and no prudential restraint from marriage.

Every organic being naturally increases at so high a rate, that, if not destroyed, the earth would soon be covered by the progeny of a single pair. Even slow-breeding man has doubled in twenty-five years, and at this rate, in less than a thousand years, there would literally not be standing-room for his progeny. Numerous cases are recorded of the astonishingly rapid increase of animals in a state of nature, when circumstances have been favourable to them during two or three following seasons. Introduced plants have become common throughout whole islands in a period of less than ten years. We may confidently assert, that all plants and animals are tending to increase at a geometrical ratio. Lighten any check, mitigate the destruction ever so little, and the number of the species will almost instantaneously increase to any amount.

The unborn, the very young, and the less vigorous suffer most from natural checks

The causes which check the natural tendency of each species to increase are most obscure. Eggs or very young animals seem to suffer most, but this is not invariably the case. With plants there is a vast destruction of seeds; seedlings suffer most from germinating in ground already thickly stocked. They also are destroyed in vast numbers by various enemies; for instance, on a piece of ground 3′ x 2′, dug and cleared, where there could be no choking from other plants, I marked all the seedlings of our native weeds as they came up, and out of 357, 295 were destroyed, chiefly by slugs and insects. More vigorous plants gradually kill the less vigorous, though fully grown plants.

Very frequently it is serving as prey to other animals which determines the average numbers of a species. Thus, the stock of partridges, grouse, and hares on any large estate depends chiefly on the destruction of vermin. If not one head of game were shot during the next twenty years in England, and no vermin were destroyed, there would, in all probability, be less game than at present, although hundreds of thousands of game animals are now annually shot.

Climate plays an important part and periodical seasons of extreme cold or drought seem to be the most effective of all checks. I estimated (chiefly from the greatly reduced number of nests in the spring) that the winter of 1854-5 destroyed four-fifths of the birds in my own grounds. In so far as climate chiefly acts in reducing food, it brings on the most severe struggle between individuals which subsist on the same kind of food. When we travel from south to north, we see some species getting rarer and finally disappearing. We are tempted to attribute the whole effect to the direct action of climate; but we forget that each species is constantly suffering enor-

mous destruction at some period of its life from enemies
or from competitors, and if these be in the least degree
favoured by any slight change of climate, they will increase in numbers, and the other species must decrease.
In Arctic regions or absolute deserts, however, the struggle
for life is almost exclusively with the elements.

When a species, owing to highly favourable circumstances, increases inordinately in numbers in a small tract,
epidemics often ensue—epidemics appear to be due to
parasitic worms which have been disproportionally favoured: and here comes in a sort of struggle between
the parasite and its prey.

*The struggle to survive is in-
cessant with all beings, and
severest between closely related ones*

Many cases are on record
showing how unexpected
are the checks and rela-
tions between organic be-
ings which have to strug-
gle together.   How important an element enclosure is, I
plainly saw in Surrey.   Here there are extensive heaths,
with a few clumps of old Scotch firs on the distant hill-
tops: within the last ten years large spaces have been
enclosed, and self-sown firs are now springing up in mul-
titudes.   On looking closely between the stems of the
heath, I found a multitude of seedlings and little trees
which had been perpetually browsed down by the cattle.
One of them, with twenty-six rings of growth, had, during
many years tried to raise its head above the stems of the
heath, but had failed.   No wonder that, as soon as the land
was enclosed, it became thickly clothed with vigorously
growing young firs.

Battle within battle must be continually recurring
with varying success; and yet in the long-run the forces
are so nicely balanced that the face of nature remains for
long periods of time uniform.   Ancient Indian ruins in
the Southern United States, which must formerly have
been cleared of trees, now display the same beautiful diversity and proportion of kinds as in the surrounding

forest. What a struggle must have gone on during long centuries between trees, each annually scattering seeds by the thousand; what war between insect and insect—between insects, snails, and other animals both with birds and beasts of prey—all striving to increase, all feeding on each other!

The struggle will almost invariably be most severe between the individuals of the same species, for they frequent the same districts, require the same food, and are exposed to the same dangers. With varieties of the same species, the struggle will be almost equally severe, and we sometimes see the contest soon decided: if several varieties of wheat be sown together, and the mixed seed be resown, some of the varieties in a few years supplant the others. As the species of the same genus usually have much similarity in habits and constitution, and always in structure, the struggle will be more severe between them than between the species of distinct genera.

The relation of organism to organism is the most important factor in determining structure

The structure of every organic being is related, in the most essential yet often hidden manner, to that of all the other organic beings with which it comes into competition or from which it has to escape or on which it preys. In the beautifully plumed seed of the dandelion, the relations seem at first confined to the elements of air and water. Yet the advantage of plumed seeds no doubt stands in the closest relation to the land being already thickly clothed with other plants; so that the seeds may be widely distributed and fall on unoccupied ground.

It is good to try in imagination to give to any one species an advantage over another. Probably in no instance should we know what to do. This ought to convince us of our ignorance on the mutual relations of all organic beings. All that we can do, is to keep steadily in mind that each being is striving to increase in a geometrical ratio; that each has to struggle for life and to suffer great destruction. When we reflect on this struggle, we may console ourselves with the full belief, that the war of nature is not incessant, that no fear is felt, that death is generally prompt, and that the vigorous, the healthy, and the happy survive and multiply.

CHAPTER IV

Natural Selection, or the Survival of the Fittest

Natural selection acts to pre-serve those organisms, which vary, however slightly, to their own advantage

How will the struggle for existence, briefly discussed in the last chapter, act in regard to variation? Can it be thought improbable that variations useful in some way to each being in the great and complex battle of life should occur in the course of many successive generations? If such do occur, can we doubt that individuals having any advantage, however slight, would have the best chance of surviving and pro-creating their kind? On the other hand, any variation in the least degree injurious would be rigidly destroyed. Variations neither useful nor injurious would not be affected by natural selection, and would be left either a fluc-tuating element, or would ultimately become fixed.

Man selects for his own good: Nature only for that of the being which she tends. Each selected character is fully exercised by her, as is implied by the fact of their selection. Man feeds a long and a short beaked pigeon on the same food; he exposes sheep with long and short wool to the same climate. How fleeting are the wishes and efforts of man! how short his time! and how poor will be his results, compared with those accumulated by Nature during whole geological periods! Can we wonder, then, that Nature's productions should be infinitely better ad-apted to the most complex conditions of life, and should plainly bear the stamp of far higher workmanship?

To effect any great amount of modification, a variety

when once formed must again, perhaps after a long interval, vary or present individual differences of the same favourable nature as before; and these must be again preserved, and so onwards. Characters and structures which we are apt to consider as of very trifling importance may thus be acted on. In plants, the down on the fruit and the colour of the flesh are considered by botanists as of the most trifling importance: yet in the United States smooth skinned fruits suffer far more from a beetle than those with down; purple plums suffer far more from a certain disease than yellow plums; another disease attacks yellow-fleshed peaches far more than those with other flesh. It is necessary to bear in mind that, owing to the law of correlation, when one part varies, and the variations are accumulated through natural selection, other modifications, often unexpected, will ensue.

As we see that those variations which under domestication appear at any particular period of life, tend to reappear in the offspring at the same period, so in a state of nature, natural selection will be enabled to modify organic beings at any age, by the accumulation of variations profitable at that age, and by their inheritance at a corresponding age.

Natural selection will modify the structure of the young in relation to the parent, and of the parent in relation to the young. What it cannot do is to modify the structure of one species, without giving it any advantage, for the good of another species. A structure used only once in an animal's life, if of high importance to it, might be modified to any extent by natural selection—for instance, the great jaws possessed by certain insects, used exclusively for opening the cocoon.

With all beings there must be much fortuitous destruction which can have little influence on the course of natural selection. For instance a vast number of eggs or seeds are annually devoured which would perhaps have yielded individuals better adapted to their conditions than those which happened to survive. If the numbers be wholly kept down as is often the case, natural selection would be powerless, but this is no valid objection to its efficiency at other times.

To make it clear how natural selection acts, I give an imaginary illustration. A wolf preys on various animals, securing some by craft, some by strength, and some by fleetness. Let us suppose that the fleetest prey, deer for instance, had increased, or that other prey had decreased during the season when the wolf was hardest pressed for food. Under such circumstances the swiftest and slimmest wolves would have the best chance of surviving and so be preserved or selected—provided they retained strength to master their prey. I may add that there are two varieties of wolf in the Catskill Mountains, one greyhound-like, which pursues deer, and the other bulky, with shorter legs, which more frequently attacks the shepherd's flocks.

Rarely single variations could be perpetuated. However, certain variations frequently recur owing to a similar organisation being similarly acted on. If the varying individual did not actually transfer to its offspring its newly-acquired character, it would transmit to them a stronger, accumulated tendency to vary in the same manner. The tendency to vary in the same manner has often been so strong that all the individuals of the same species have been similarly modified without the aid of any form of selection. Or only a third, fifth, or tenth part of the individuals may have been thus affected. If the variation were of a beneficial nature, the original form would be supplanted by the modified form, through the survival of the fittest.

Most animals and plants keep to their proper homes and do not needlessly wander about; we see this even with migratory birds, which almost always return to the same spot. Consequently each newly formed variety would generally be at first local, so that similarly modified individuals would soon exist in a small body together, and would often breed together. If the new variety were successful in its battle for life, it would slowly spread, competing with and conquering the unchanged individuals on the margins of an ever-increasing circle.

Sexual selection favors the most vigorous males, or those equipped with weapons or adornments useful in the rivalry for females

It is possible for the two sexes to be modified through natural selection in relation to different habits of life, or for one sex to be modified in relation to the other sex, as commonly occurs. This leads me to say a few words on Sexual Selection, which depends on a struggle between the individuals of one sex. Generally, the most vigorous males, those which are best fitted for their places in nature, will leave most progeny. But in many cases, victory depends on having special weapons confined to the male sex. A hornless stag or spurless cock would have a poor chance of leaving numerous offspring. How low in the scale of nature the law of battle descends, I know not; male alligators have been described as fighting, bellowing, and whirling round, like Indians in a war dance, for the possession of the females; male salmons have been observed fighting all day. The war is, perhaps, severest between the males of polygamous animals, and these seem oftenest provided with special weapons. Special means of defence may be given, for the shield may be as important for victory, as the spear.

Amongst birds, the contest is often of more peaceful character. There is the severest rivalry in many species to attract, by singing, the females. The rock-thrush of Guiana, birds of paradise, and some others, congregate; and successive males display with the most elaborate care, and show off in the best manner, their gorgeous plumage; they likewise perform strange antics before the females, which, standing by as spectators, at last choose the most attractive partner. Female birds, by selecting, during thousands of generations, the most melodious or beautiful males, according to their standard of beauty, might produce a marked effect. I believe that when males and females have the same habits of life but differ in structure, colour, or ornament, such differences have been mainly caused by sexual selection.

Since intercrossing is indispensable for preserving vigour and fertility, adaptations to insure crossing are extremely general in nature

I must here introduce a short digression. All vertebrate animals, all insects, and some other large groups of animals, pair for each birth. Still there are many hermaphrodite animals which do not habitually pair, and a vast majority of plants are hermaphrodites. What reason is there for supposing that in these cases two individuals ever concur in reproduction?

In the first place, a cross between different varieties or strains gives vigour and fertility to the offspring; *close* interbreeding diminishes vigour and fertility. These facts alone incline me to believe that it is a general law of nature that no organic being fertilises itself for a perpetuity of generations; a cross is occasionally—perhaps at long intervals—indispensable.

On this belief we can understand several large classes of facts which on any other view are inexplicable. Every hybridizer knows how unfavourable exposure to wet is to fertilisation, yet what a multitude of flowers have their anthers and stigmas exposed to the weather! The fullest freedom for the entrance of pollen from another individual will explain the exposure. Many flowers, on the other hand, have their organs of fructification closely enclosed, but these almost invariably present beautiful and curious adaptations in relation to the visits of insects, and their fertility is greatly diminished if these visits be prevented.

When the stamens of a flower suddenly spring towards

the pistil, the contrivance seems adapted solely to ensure self-fertilisation; but the agency of insects is often required to cause the stamens to spring forward, as with the barbery; and this genus seems to have a special contrivance for self-fertilisation, but if closely-allied forms are planted near, it is hardly possible to raise pure seedlings, so largely do they naturally cross. In numerous other cases, there are special contrivances which effectually prevent the stigma receiving pollen from its own flower. In many cases either the anthers burst before the stigma is ready for fertilisation, or the stigma is ready before the pollen, so that these plants have in fact separated sexes, and must habitually be crossed. How strange that the pollen and stigmatic surface, though placed as if for self-fertilisation, should be in so many cases mutually useless to each other! How simply are these facts explained on the view of an occasional cross with a distinct individual being advantageous or indispensable!

I raised 233 seedling cabbages from some plants of different varieties; only 78 were true to their kind. Yet the pistil of each flower is surrounded not only by its own stamens but by those of the many other flowers on the same plant; and the pollen of each flower readily gets on its own stigma without insect agency; for plants carefully protected from insects produce the full number of pods. How, then, comes it that such a vast number of the seedlings are mongrelized? It must arise from the pollen of a distinct *variety* having a prepotent effect over the flower's own pollen; and that this is part of the general law of good being derived from the intercrossing of distinct individuals of the same species.

As yet I have not found a single terrestrial animal which can fertilise itself. This remarkable fact is intelligible on the view of an occasional cross being indispensable; for there are no means by which an occasional cross could be effected without the concurrence of two individuals. Of aquatic animals, there are many self-fertilising hermaphrodites; but currents of water offer an obvious means for an occasional cross.

A large number of individuals, intercrossing, and isolation all favour the production of new forms

A great amount of variability, under which term individual differences are always included, will evidently be favourable for new forms. A large number of individuals, by giving a better chance within any given period for the appearance of profitable variations, will compensate for a lesser amount of variability in each individual, and is an important element of success. Nature does not grant an indefinite period; if any one species does not become modified and improved in a corresponding degree with its competitors, it will be exterminated.

Within a confined area, with some place in the natural polity not perfectly occupied, all individuals varying in the right direction, though in different degrees, will tend to be preserved. But if the area be large, its districts will almost certainly present different conditions of life; then, if the same species undergoes modification in different districts, the newly-formed varieties will intercross on the confines of each. Intercrossing will chiefly affect those animals which unite for each birth and wander much, and which do not breed at a very quick rate. Hence with animals of this nature, for instance, birds, varieties will generally be confined to separated countries. With hermaphrodite organisms which cross only occasionally, and likewise with animals which unite for each birth, but wander little and can increase at a rapid rate, a new and improved variety might be quickly formed on any one spot, and might there maintain itself in a body and afterwards spread, so that the individuals of the new variety would chiefly cross together.

We must not assume that free intercrossing would always eliminate the effects of natural selection; for within the same area, two varieties of the same animal may

long remain distinct, from haunting different stations,
from breeding at slightly different seasons, or from the
individuals of each variety preferring to pair together.

Intercrossing plays a very important part in nature
by keeping individuals of the same species or variety uniform in character. Even if occasional intercrossings take
place only at long intervals, the young thus produced
will gain so much in vigour and fertility that they will
have a better chance of surviving and propagating their
kind; and thus the influence of crosses, even at rare intervals, will be great. With respect to organic beings extremely low in the scale, which cannot possibly intercross,
uniformity can be given to the modified offspring solely
by natural selection preserving similar favourable variations.

Isolation is important in the modification of species.
In a smaller confined area, conditions will be almost uniform; so that natural selection will tend to modify individuals of the same species in the same manner. Intercrossing with the inhabitants of the surrounding districts
will also be prevented. After any physical change in
conditions, such as of climate, elevation of the land, etc.,
isolation prevents the immigration of better adapted organisms; and thus new places will be left open to modifications of the old inhabitants. Lastly, isolation will give
time for a new variety to be improved at a slow rate.

*But large areas, affording
wide competition, produce
the most dominant forms*

Largeness of area is still
more important, especially
for species which shall
prove capable of enduring
long and spreading widely. Conditions are much more
complex from the large number of existing species; if
some of these become improved, others will have to be
improved in a corresponding degree, or be exterminated.
Each new form, also, as soon as it has been much improved, will be able to spread over the continuous area,

and will thus come into competition with many other forms. Moreover, great areas, though now continuous, will often, owing to former oscillations of level, have existed in a broken condition; so that the good effects of isolation will generally, to a certain extent, have occurred. Finally, modification will generally have been more rapid in large areas; and what is more important, new forms which already have been victorious over many competitors, will be those that will spread most widely, and will give rise to the greatest number of new varieties and species. They will thus play a more important part in the changing history of the organic world. In accordance with this view, we can understand the fact of the reproductions of the smaller continent of Australia now yielding before those of the Europaeo-Asiatic area.

Natural selection will generally act very slowly, only at long intervals of time, and only on a few of the inhabitants of the same region. These slow, intermittent results accord well with what geology tells us of the manner in which the inhabitants of the world have changed. As favoured forms increase, the less favoured become rare, and rarity, geology tells us, is the precursor to extinction. Any form with few individuals will run a good chance of extinction during great fluctuations in the seasons, or from a temporary increase of enemies. Forms in closest competition with those undergoing improvement will naturally suffer most.

Natural selection leads to species diverging into genera, for by wide diversification a maximum of forms find places in the economy of nature

According to my view, varieties are species in the process of formation. How, then, does the lesser difference between varieties become augmented into the greater difference between species? Mere chance might cause one variety to differ in some character from its parents, and the offspring to differ in the same character and in a greater degree; but this alone would never account for the great difference between species of the same genus.

As has always been my practice, I have sought light from our domestic productions. On the acknowledged principle that "fanciers do not and will not admire a medium standard, but like extremes," two fanciers go on (as has actually occurred with the sub-breeds of the tumbler-pigeon) choosing and breeding from birds with longer and longer beaks, or with shorter and shorter beaks. Ultimately, after the lapse of centuries, these sub-breeds would become converted into distinct breeds. As the difference became greater, animals with intermediate characters would not have been used for breeding, and will have tended to disappear. Here, then, we see the principle of divergence causing differences steadily to increase and the breeds to diverge both from each other and from their common parents.

But how can any analogous principle apply in nature? I believe it can and does apply from the simple circum- stance that the more diversified the descendants become, the better can they seize on places in the polity of nature, and so increase in numbers. Take the case of a carnivorous quadruped, of which the number that can be supported in any country has long ago arrived at its full average. It can succeed in increasing only by its varying descendants seizing on places at present occupied by other animals: some of them, for instance, being enabled to feed on new kinds of prey, some climbing trees, frequenting water, and some perhaps becoming less carnivorous. The more diversified the descendants become, the more places they will be enabled to occupy. So it will be with plants. Where they come into the closest competition, the advantages of diversification of structure determine that the inhabitants shall, as a general rule, belong to what we call different genera and orders. The advantage of diversification is, in fact, the same as that of the physiological division of labour. A stomach adapted to digest vegetable matter alone, or flesh alone, draws most nutriment from these substances. So in the economy of any land, the more perfectly the animal and plants are diversified, the greater will be the number of individuals capable of there supporting themselves.

The principle of benefit derived from divergence will generally lead to the most divergent variations being preserved and accumulated by natural selection. Varieties will generally be exposed to the same conditions which made their parents variable, and the tendency to variability is itself hereditary. Thus modified descendants will generally go on increasing in number and diverging in character, though a medium form may often long endure, for selection acts according to the nature of the places which are not perfectly occupied by other beings.

Improved forms eliminate the competing intermediate forms, as well as the parent forms

But during the process of modification, another principle, extinction, will have played an important part. The improved descendants will constantly tend to supplant and exterminate their predecessors, for competition will be most severe between those forms most nearly related in habits and structure. Hence intermediate forms, as well as original parent-species, will generally tend to become extinct.

We may go further than this. It seems extremely probable that they will replace, and thus exterminate, also some of the original species most nearly related to their parents. As two groups go on diverging in different directions, and as they eliminate the species intermediate between them, the once new species will have to be ranked as distinct genera, or even sub-families. Thus genera are produced by descent with modification, from two or more species of the same genus. I see no reason to limit the process of modification to the formation of genera alone.

Looking remotely to the future, we may predict that,

owing to the steady increase of the larger groups, a multitude of smaller groups will become extinct, leaving no modified descendants; and consequently, of the species living at any one period, extremely few will transmit descendants to a remote futurity.

Natural Selection acts exclusively by the preservation and accumulation of beneficial variations. This improvement inevitably leads to the gradual advancement of the organisation of the greater number of living beings. But naturalists have not defined to each other's satisfaction what is meant by an advance in organisation. Amongst the vertebrata the degree of intellect and an approach in structure to man clearly come into play. Von Baer's standard seems best, namely, the amount of differentiation of the parts of the same being, in the adult state as I should be inclined to add, and their specialisation for different functions. All physiologists admit that the specialisation of organs is an advantage; hence specialisation is within the scope of natural selection. On the other hand, it is quite possible for natural selection gradually to fit a being to a situation in which several organs would be superfluous: in such cases there would be retrogression in organisation.

On our theory the continued existence of lowly organisms offers no difficulty. What advantage would it be to an earthworm, to be highly organised? If it were no advantage, these worms would be left, by natural selection, unimproved or but little improved. And geology tells us that some of the lowest forms have remained for an enormous period in nearly their present state. But to suppose that most low forms have not advanced since the first dawn of life would be extremely rash; every naturalist who has dissected beings ranked as very low must have been struck with their really wondrous and beautiful organisation. However, the high advancement of certain whole classes, or of certain members of each class, does not at all necessarily lead to the extinction of those groups with which they do not enter into close competition.

What then checks an indefinite increase in the number of species? If an area be inhabited by very many species, each or nearly each species will be represented by few individuals. The process of extermination in such cases would be rapid, whereas the production of new species must always be slow. When any species become very rare, close interbreeding will help to exterminate it. Lastly, and this I think most important, a dominant species, which has already beaten many competitors in its own home, will tend to spread and supplant many others and thus check the inordinate increase of specific forms throughout the world.

On the principles of divergence and extinction, the orderly interrelationships of all organic beings can be explained

It is a truly wonderful fact—the wonder of which we are apt to overlook from familiarity—that all animals and all plants throughout all time and space should be related to each other in groups, subordinate to groups, varieties of the same species most closely related, species of the same genus less closely related, species of distinct genera much less closely, and genera forming families, orders, and classes. If species had been independently created, no explanation of this would have been possible; but it is explained through inheritance and the complex action of natural selection, entailing extinction and divergence of character.

The affinities of all the beings of the same class have sometimes been represented by a great tree. The green and budding twigs may represent existing species; all the growing twigs have tried to branch out on all sides, and to overtop surrounding twigs and branches, in the same manner as species have at all times overmastered other species in the great battle for life. The limbs divided into great branches, and these into lesser and lesser branches, were themselves once budding twigs. Of the many twigs which flourished when the tree was a mere bush, only two or three, now grown into great branches, survive and bear other branches; many a limb and branch has decayed and dropped off; and these represent those whole orders, families, and genera now known to us only in a fossil state. As buds give rise by growth to fresh buds, and these, if vigorous, overtop many a feebler branch, so it has been with the great Tree of Life, which fills with its dead and broken branches the crust of the earth, and covers the surface with its ever-branching and beautiful ramifications.

CHAPTER V

Laws of Variation

*Though the causes of varia-
tion are unknown, changes in
conditions, as well as use and
disuse, seem to stimulate variations*

The fact of variations oc-
curring much more fre-
quently under domestica-
tion, and the greater variability of species having
wide ranges, lead to the
conclusion that variability is related to the conditions of
life during several successive generations. It is very
difficult to decide how far changed conditions have acted
in a definite manner. Thus, it is well known to furriers
that animals of the same species have thicker and better
fur the further north they live; but who can tell how much
of this difference may be due to the warmest-clad individuals having been preserved, and how much to the action
of climate? for it would appear that climate has some
direct action on the hair of our domestic quadrupeds.
Similar varieties have been produced under external conditions as different as can well be conceived; and dissimilar varieties, under apparently the same conditions.
Again, innumerable instances are known of species not
varying at all under the most opposite of climates. Such
considerations incline me to lay less weight on the action
of the surrounding conditions, than on a tendency to vary,
due to causes of which we are quite ignorant.

It is probable that the nearly wingless condition of
several ground feeding birds, now inhabiting oceanic
islands tenanted by no beast of prey, has been caused by
disuse. In some cases we might put down to disuse modifi-

39

cations of structure which are mainly due to natural selection. The eyes of moles and of some burrowing rodents are rudimentary in size, and in some cases covered by skin and fur. As frequent inflammation of the eyes must be injurious to any animal, and as eyes are certainly not necessary to animals having subterranean habits, a reduction of their size, with the adhesion of the eyelids and growth of fur over them, might be an advantage; if so, natural selection would aid the effects of disuse.

It is common for species of the same genus to inhabit hot and cold countries. If species of the same genus are descended from a single parent-form, acclimatisation must be effected during a long course of descent. Species from an arctic or even from a temperate region cannot endure a tropical climate, or conversely, but the degree of adaptation of species to the climates under which they live is often overrated. The extraordinary capacity in our domestic animals of not only withstanding the most different climates, but of being perfectly fertile (a far severer test) under them, may be used as an argument that other animals could easily be brought to bear widely different climates. The rat and mouse have been transported by man to the cold climate of Faroe in the north and many an island in the torrid zones.

Some variations are governed by principles of correlation and economy, often operating in terms of natural selection

When slight variations in any one part occur and are accumulated through natural selection, other parts become modified. Variations of structure arising in the young or larvae naturally tend to affect the structure of the mature animal. Parts of the body which are homologous seem eminently liable to vary in a like manner: For example, the front and hind legs vary together.

A striking case of correlation appears in many pelargoniums. The two upper petals in the central flower often lose their patches of darker colour. When this occurs, the adherent nectary is aborted; when the colour is absent from only one of the petals, the nectary is not aborted but much shortened. Hence modifications of structure may be wholly due to the laws of variation and correlation, without being, as far as we can judge, of the slightest service to the species. We often attribute to correlated variation structures which are simply due to inheritance; an ancient progenitor may have acquired one modification, and, after thousands of generations, some independent modification; these two would be thought to be in some necessary manner correlated. Some correlations are apparently due to the manner in which natural selection can alone act. For instance, winged seeds are never found in fruits which do not open; unless the capsules were open the seeds could gain no advantage. As Goethe expressed the law of compensation, or balance of growth, "in order to spend on one side, nature is forced to economise on the other side." Thus it is difficult to get a cow to give much milk and to fatten readily. I suspect, also, that some cases of compensation may be merged under a more general principle that natural selection is continually trying to economise every part. I can thus only understand a fact with which I am struck, that when a cirripede is parasitic within another cirripede it loses more or less completely its own shell. Now the saving of a large and complex structure would be a decided advantage, for each individual would have a better chance of supporting itself by less nutriment being wasted. Natural selection will tend to reduce any part as soon as it becomes superfluous.

Multiple, rudimentary, highly developed structures and those which differ in allied species are often extremely variable

When any part is repeated many times in the same individual (as the vertebrae in snakes) the number is variable; whereas the same part, when it occurs in lesser numbers, is constant. As "vegetable repeti-

tion" is a sign of low organisation, beings low in the scale
of nature are more variable than those which are higher.
Lowness here means that the several parts have been little
specialised: as long as the same part has to perform
diversified work, we can see why selection should not pre-
serve or reject each little deviation so carefully.

The variability of rudimentary parts results from
their uselessness, and consequently from natural selection
having no power to check deviations. An abnormally
developed part tends to be highly variable. The rule
applies only to a part unusually developed in comparison
with the same part in closely allied species. Thus, the
wing of a bat is a most abnormal structure in mammals,
but the rule would apply only if some one species of bat
had wings developed remarkably in comparison with the
other species. The rule applies very strongly in the case
of unusual secondary sexual characters attached to one
sex, but not directly connected with reproduction.

When we see any part developed in a remarkable
manner, the presumption is that it is of high importance:
nevertheless it is in this case eminently liable to variation.
Why should this be so? On the view that groups of species have been modified through natural selection, I think
we can obtain some light. If, in our domestic animals, no
selection be applied, the breed will cease to have a uniform character and may be said to be degenerating. In
rudimentary organs and in those but little specialised,
we see a parallel, for natural selection has not or cannot
come into full play, and the organisation is left in a
fluctuating condition. But those points in our domestic
animals which are undergoing rapid change by continued
selection are also eminently liable to variation. Even in
the same sub-breed, as in the short-faced tumbler pigeon,
it is notoriously difficult to breed nearly perfect birds,
many departing widely from the standard. A constant
struggle goes on between the tendency to reversion, an in-
nate tendency to new variations, and the power of steady

selection to keep the breed true. In the long run selection gains the day.

Now let us turn to nature. When a part has been developed in an extraordinary manner in any one species, we may conclude it has undergone an extraordinary amount of modification since the several species branched off from the common progenitor. Extraordinary modification implies unusually large and long-continued variability, continually accumulated by natural selection for the benefit of the species. We might expect to find more variability in such parts than in parts which have remained constant for a much longer period. And this, I am convinced, is the case. That the struggle between natural selection on the one hand, and the tendency to reversion and variability on the other hand, will in the course of time cease; and that the most abnormally developed organs may be made constant, I see no reason to doubt. Hence, when an organ has been transmitted to many modified descendants, as the wing of the bat, it must have existed for an immense period in nearly the same stage. It is only in cases in which modification has been comparatively recent and extraordinarily great that we ought to find *generative variability*, for it will seldom as yet have been fixed by the continued selection of beneficial variations.

If in a genus of plants some species had blue flowers and some red, the colour would be a specific character, and no one would be surprised at one of the blue varying into red; but if all the species had blue flowers, the colour would become a generic character, and its variation would be more unusual. When some important organ generally constant throughout a large group of species, *differs* considerably in closely-allied species, it is often *variable* in the individuals of the same species. The more an organ normally differs in the different species of the same group, the more subject it is to anomalies in the individuals.

As generic characters have been inherited before the several species branched off from their common progenitor, it is not probable they should vary at the present day.

Species of the same group differ more widely in their secondary sexual characters than in other parts, for sexual selection is less rigid than ordinary selection, as it does not entail death, but only gives fewer offspring to less favoured males. It may thus have succeeded in giving to the species of the same group a greater amount of difference in these than in other respects.

Secondary differences between the two sexes are generally displayed in the very same parts in which the species of the same genus differ from each other. This relation has a clear meaning on my view: whatever part of the common progenitor became variable, variations of this part would be taken advantage of by natural and sexual selection, to fit species to their places in nature, and likewise to fit the two sexes of the same species to each other, or to fit the males to struggle for possession of the females.

A variety of one species often assumes a character proper to an allied species, or reverts to some characters of an early progenitor. The most distinct breeds of pigeon, in countries widely apart, present sub-varieties with reversed feathers on the head and feathers on the feet—characters not possesed by the aboriginal rock-pigeon. Such analogous variations are due to the several races having inherited from a common parent the same constitution and tendency to variation. However, we have another case, the occasional appearance in all breeds of slaty-blue pigeons with two black bars on the wings, white loins, and a bar at the end of the tail. As all these marks are characteristic of the parent rock-pigeon, this is a case of reversion, and not of a new yet analogous variation.

It is very surprising that characters should reappear after having been lost for hundreds of generations. After twelve generations, the proportion of blood from one ancestor is only 1 to 2048, and yet a tendency to reversion is retained. In a breed in which *both* parents have lost some character their progenitor possessed, the tendency might be transmitted for almost any number of generations. The most probable hypotheses is that the character has been lying latent, and at last, under unknown favourable conditions, is developed. The improbability of such a tendency is not greater than that of rudimentary organs being similarly transmitted.

CHAPTER VI

Difficulties of the Theory

No difficulty seems fatal to the theory

Long before this a crowd of difficulties will have occurred to the reader. Some are so serious that to this day I can hardly reflect on them without being staggered; but, to the best of my judgment, the greater number are only apparent and those that are real are not, I think, fatal to the theory.

First, why, if species have descended by fine gradations, do we not everywhere see transitional forms, instead of the species being, as we see them, well defined? Secondly, could an animal having, for instance, the structure and habits of a bat, have been formed by the modification of some other widely different animal? Could natural selection produce an organ such as the tail of a giraffe, which serves as a fly-flapper, and, on the other hand, an organ so wonderful as the eye? Thirdly, can instincts be acquired and modified through natural selection? Fourthly, how can we account for species, when crossed, being sterile and producing sterile offspring, whereas, when varieties are crossed, their fertility is unimpaired?

Few transitional forms are found, because their range and number of individuals are so limited as to prevent their long survival

Extinction and natural selection go hand in hand. Hence, both parent and transitional varieties will generally have been exterminated by the very perfection of the new form. Why do we not find them embedded in countless numbers in the crust of the earth?

I believe the answer mainly lies in the <u>geological record</u> <u>being incomparably less perfect than is generally supposed</u>.

But when close-allied species inhabit the same territory, we surely ought at the present time to find transitional forms. Let us take a simple case: from north to south over a continent, representative species often meet and interlock; as one becomes rarer, the other becomes more frequent, till one replaces the other. But where they intermingle, these species are generally as distinct from each other in every detail as are specimens from the metropolis inhabited by each. Why do we not find intermediate varieties?

As climate and height or depth graduate away insensibly we see that the range of the inhabitants of any country by no means exclusively depends on physical conditions, but in large part on the presence of other, already defined species, on which it lives, by which it is destroyed, or with which it competes. Its range will thus tend to be sharply defined. Moreover, each species on the confines of its range, where it exists in lessened numbers, will, during fluctuations in the number of its enemies or of its prey, or in the seasons, be extremely liable to utter extermination; and thus its range will be still more sharply defined.

As varieties do not essentially differ from species, the same rule will probably apply to both. And it would appear from information given me by Mr. Watson, Dr. Asa Gray, and Mr. Wollaston, that intermediate varieties between two forms are much rarer numerically than the forms they connect. <u>The intermediate form would be eminently liable to inroads of closely-allied forms on both sides</u>. But far more important, during the process of modification by which two varieties are converted and perfected into distinct species—the two which exist in larger numbers will have a great advantage over the intermediate variety. For forms existing in larger numbers will have a better chance of presenting favourable variations for natural selection to seize on.

Species do not present a chaos of intermediate links because new varieties are very slowly formed and new places depend on slow changes, so that, in any one region at any one time, we ought to see only a few species presenting slight modifications of structure in some degree permanent. And lastly, the very process of natural selection constantly tends to exterminate the parent forms and the intermediate links.

By a long accumulation of adaptive modifications a species may change vastly, or develop very perfect or very remarkable organs

How could a land carnivorous animal have been converted into one with aquatic habits? It would be easy to show that there now exist carnivorous animals presenting close intermediate grades from strictly terrestrial habits. Look at the family of squirrels; we have the finest gradation from animals with their tails only slightly flattened to flying squirrels with their limbs and the base of the tail united by a broad expanse of skin, which allows them to glide through the air to an astonishing distance. I see no difficulty in the continued preservation of individuals with fuller and fuller flank-membranes, until a perfect flying squirrel was produced. If about a dozen genera of birds were to become extinct, who would surmise that birds might have existed which used their wings solely as fins in water or front legs on land, like the penguin, or as sails, like the ostrich? In North America the black bear was seen by Hearne swimming for hours with widely open mouth, thus catching, almost like a whale, insects in the water.

To suppose that the eye with all its inimitable contrivances for adjusting the focus to different distances, for admitting different amounts of light, and for the correction of spherical and chromatic aberration, could have been formed by natural selection, seems, I freely confess, absurd in the highest degree. The simplest organ which can be called an eye consists of an optic nerve surrounded by pigment-cells and covered by translucent skin, but without any lens or other refractive body. Even lower, we find aggregates of pigmented cells as organs of vision, without any nerves. In certain star-fishes, small depressions in the pigment which surrounds the nerve are filled with gelatinous matter, projecting like the cornea in higher animals. This serves only to concentrate the luminous rays. We thus gain by far the most important step towards the formation of a true, picture-forming eye; for we have only to place the naked extremity of the optic nerve, in some lower animals deeply buried in the body and in some near the surface, at the right distance from the concentrating apparatus, and an image will be formed on it.

When we reflect on the graduated range of structure in the eyes of lower animals the difficulty ceases to be great in believing that natural selection may have converted an optic nerve, coated with pigment and invested by transparent membrane, into an optical instrument as perfect as is possessed by any of the Articulate Class. He who will go thus far ought to admit that a structure as perfect as an eagle's eye might thus be formed, although he does not know the transitional states. The contraction of the iris and the muscular movements of the eye are not essential, but only improvements which might have been added at any stage. Even in man, the beautiful crystalline lens is formed in the embryo by an accumulation of epidermic cells, lying in a sack-like fold of the skin; and the vitreous body is formed from sub-cutaneous tissue.

We compare the eye with a telescope. But have we any right to assume that the Creator works by intellectual ＞ powers like those of man? If we must compare the eye to an optical instrument, we ought in imagination to take a thick layer of transparent tissue with spaces filled with fluid, and then suppose every part to be continually separating into layers of different densities and thickness, placed at different distances from each other, and with the surfaces of each layer slowly changing in form. Further we must suppose that there is a power, represented by natural selection always intently watching each slight alteration in the transparent layers; and carefully preserving each which, in any way or in any degree, tends to produce a distincter image. Let this process go on for millions of years; and during each year on millions of individuals of many kinds; and may we not believe that a living optical instrument might thus be formed as superior to one of glass, as the works of the Creator are to those of man?

In numerous instances among lower animals the same organ performs different functions. The Hydra may be turned inside out, and the exterior surface will then digest and the stomach respire. In such cases natural selection might specialise an organ for one function alone, and thus greatly change its nature.

Again, two distinct organs, or the same organ under two very different forms, may simultaneously perform the same function, and this is an extremely important means of transition—there are fish with gills that breathe air dissolved in water, at the same time they breathe free air in their swimbladders. Plants climb by spirally twining, by clasping a support with tendrils, or by aerial rootlets; these three means are usually found in distinct groups, but some few species exhibit two of the means or even all three in the same individual.

The illustration of the swimbladder in fishes is a good one, because it shows us that an organ originally constructed for one purpose, flotation, may be converted into one for a widely different purpose, respirations. The swimbladder is homologous, or "ideally similar" with the lungs of the higher vertebrate animals. It may be inferred that all vertebrate animals with true lungs are descended from an ancient and unknown prototype, which was furnished with a floating apparatus or swimbladder. In the higher Vertebrata the gills have wholly disappeared—but in the embryo the slits on the sides of the neck still mark their former position.

Although we must be extremely cautious in concluding that any organ could not have been produced by successive gradations, yet serious cases of difficulty occur. The electric organs of fishes offer special difficulty; for it is impossible to conceive by what steps these wondrous organs have been produced. It is generally admitted that there exists between them and ordinary muscle a close analogy. Also muscular contraction is accompanied by an electrical discharge; and, as Dr. Radcliffe insists, "the discharge of the torpedo may be only another form of the discharge which attends upon the action of muscle and motor nerve." Beyond this point we cannot at present go. The luminous organs which occur in a few insects offer a difficulty almost exactly parallel with that of the electric organ.

In all cases of beings, far removed from each other in organisation but furnished with similar and peculiar organs, fundamental differences can always be detected. As two men have sometimes independently hit on the same invention, so natural selection has produced similar organs, as far as function is concerned, in distinct organic beings. It is a common rule throughout nature that the same end should be gained, even in closely related beings, by the most diversified means. Bivalve shells are made to open and shut, but on what a number of patterns is the hinge constructed. Seeds are disseminated by their minuteness, by their capsule being converted into a balloon, by being embedded in flesh, by having hooks and grapnels of many kinds, and by being furnished with wings and plumes as different in shape as they are elegant in structure, so as to be wafted by every breeze.

The Coryanthes orchid has part of its lower lip hollowed into a bucket, into which drops of water fall from two secreting horns above it; when the bucket is half full, the water overflows by a spout on one side. The part over the bucket is hollowed into a chamber, within which are curious fleshy ridges. Dr. Cruger saw crowds of bees visiting this orchid to gnaw off these ridges. They frequently pushed each other into the bucket, and their wings being thus wetted they could not fly, but were compelled to crawl out through the spout. Dr. Cruger saw a "continual procession" of bees crawling out of their involuntary bath. The passage is narrow, and a bee, in forcing its way out, first rubs its back against the stigma and then against the pollen-masses which are thus glued to the bee which first crawls out through the passage. Dr. Cruger sent me a flower in spirits of wine, with a bee which he had killed before it had quite crawled out with a pollen-mass still fastened to its back. When the bee, thus provided, flies to another flower, is pushed into the bucket, and then crawls out the passage; the pollen-mass necessarily comes first into contact with the stigma and the flower is fertilised.

The tail of the giraffe looks like a fly-flapper; and it seems incredible that this could have been adapted for so trifling an object; yet we know that the existence of cattle and other animals in South America absolutely depends on their power of resisting the attacks of insects.

We may easily err in believing characters have been developed through natural selection. Structures indirectly gained may subsequently have been taken advantage of under newly acquired habits. If green woodpeckers had existed, we should have thought the colour was an important adaptation through natural selection to conceal this bird from its enemies; as it is, the colour is probably due to sexual selection. The sutures in the skulls of young mammals have been advanced as adaptations for aiding parturition, but as sutures occur in young birds and reptiles, which only escape from a broken egg, we may infer they have arisen from the laws of growth, and been taken advantage of in the parturition of higher animals.

Organisms develop beautiful or perfect structures only in so far as these structures are useful in the struggle for survival

Some naturalists believe that many structures have been created for the sake of beauty, to delight man or the Creator (but this point is beyond the scope of scientific discussion). I may first remark that the idea of what is beautiful is not unalterable. Men of different races admire entirely different beauty in their women. If beautiful objects had been created solely for man's gratification, it ought to be shown that before man appeared, there was less beauty on the face of the earth. Flowers rank among the most beautiful productions of nature, but a flower fertilized by the wind never has a gaily-coloured corolla. We may conclude that, if insects had not been developed our plants would have produced only such poor flowers as we see on our fir and oak, and on grasses and nettles, which are all fertilised through the wind. A great number of male animals, as all our most gorgeous birds, some fishes, reptiles, and mammals, and a host of magnificently coloured butterflies, have been rendered beautiful for beauty's sake; but this has been effected through sexual selection. So it is with the music of birds.

Natural selection cannot produce any modification exclusively for the good of another species, but it can, for injury of other animals. Natural selection will never produce in a being any structure more injurious than beneficial to that being. If any part comes to be injurious, it will be modified or the being will become extinct. Natural selection tends only to make each being as perfect as, or slightly more perfect than, those with which it comes into competition. This is the standard of perfection attained under nature. Can we consider as perfect the elaboration of dense clouds of pollen by our fir-trees, so that a few granules may be wafted by chance on to the ovules? It may be difficult, but we ought to admire the savage instinctive hatred of the queen-bee, which urges her to destroy the young queens, her daughters, as soon as they are born! This is for the good of the community and maternal love or maternal hatred is all the same to the inexorable principle of natural selection.

CHAPTER VII

Miscellaneous Objections
to the Theory of Natural Selection

Selection modifies structures for uses we do not always perceive, and changes induced independently of natural selection may become fixed

A serious objection has been urged by Bronn, the German translator of this work, that many characters appear to be of no service whatever to their possessors, and therefore cannot have been influenced through natural selection. We ought, first, to be extremely cautious in deciding what structures are, or have formerly been of use. Second, when one part is modified, so will be other parts, through certain dimly seen causes, such as an increased or diminished flow of nutriment to a part. Third, we have to allow for the action of changed conditions of life. If we bear in mind the power of a minute drop of poison in producing complex galls, we ought not to feel too sure that variations are not the effect of some local change in the nature of the sap, due to some change in the condition. If the unknown cause were to act persistently, all the individuals of the species would be similarly modified.

As Bronn gives the length of the ears in mice as an instance of differences in structure which can be of no special use, I may mention that the external ears of the common mouse are supplied in an extraordinary manner with nerves, so that they no doubt serve as tactile organs; hence the length can hardly be quite unimportant. Again, orchids present a multitude of curious structures, which a few years ago would have been considered without any special function; but they are now known to be of the highest importance for fertilisation.

In numerous cases we find modification of structure affecting only some of the flowers on the same plant. Such changes may be attributed to the laws of growth and the inter-action of parts, independently of natural selection. Can it be said of these variations, that the plants have been caught in the act of progressing? On the contrary, I should infer from the parts differing greatly on the same plant, that such modifications were of extremely small importance to the plants and would thus not have been accumulated through natural selection. A structure when it ceases to be of service, generally becomes variable, as we see with rudimentary organs, for it will no longer be regulated by selection. But when modifications have been induced which are unimportant, they may be transmitted to numerous, otherwise modified, descendants. It cannot have been important to most mammals, birds, or reptiles, whether they were clothed with hair, feathers or scales; yet hair has been transmitted to mammals, feathers to birds, and scales to reptiles. Thus, I believe, differences which we consider important first appeared in many cases as fluctuating variations, which became constant through the nature of the organism and of the surrounding conditions, as well as through the intercrossing of distinct individuals, but not through natural selection, as they do not affect the welfare of the species. It is a strange result that characters of slight importance to the species, are the most important to the systematist.

Natural selection is competent to account for the incipient stages of useful structures

A distinguished zoologist, Mr. St. George Mivart, has recently collected all the objections advanced by myself and others against the theory of natural selection, and has illustrated them with admirable art and force. They make a formidable array, as it forms no part of Mr. Mivart's plan to give facts and considerations opposed to his conclusions. My judgment may not be trustworthy, but after reading Mr. Mivart's book and comparing each section with what I have said on the same head, I never before felt so convinced of the truth of my conclusions. The one new point which struck many readers is, "that natural selection is incompetent to account for the incipient stages of useful structures." I will here consider cases advanced by Mr. Mivart, selecting the most illustrative.

The giraffe, by its lofty stature, elongated neck, fore-legs, head and tongue, has its whole frame beautifully adapted for browsing on the higher branches of trees. Slight proportional differences are not of the slightest use to most species. But with the nascent giraffe, because of its habits of life, those individuals which were able during dearths to reach even an inch or two above the others would generally have survived and left offspring inherit-ing the same bodily peculiarities, or with a tendency to vary again in the same manner. By this process long-continued, combined in a most important manner with the inherited effects of increased use of parts, it seems that an ordinary hoofed quadruped might be converted into a giraffe.

Mr. Mivart brings forward two objections. One is that the increased size of body would require increased food, and he considers it as "very problematical whether the disadvantages would, in times of scarcity, counter-balance the advantages." But as the giraffe does actually exist in large numbers in South Africa, why should he doubt that intermediate gradations could formerly have existed there? Increased bulk would act as a protection against beasts of prey, and its tall neck would serve as a watch-tower. This animal also uses its neck for offence or defence, by violently swinging its head armed with stump-like horns. The preservation of each species can rarely be determined by any one advantage, but by the union of all, great and small.

Mr. Mivart then asks if high browsing be so great an advantage, why have not more quadrupeds acquired a lofty stature? In every meadow in England, we see the lower branches of trees planed to an exact level by browsing cattle; what advantage would it be to sheep, if kept there, to acquire slightly longer necks? In South Africa the competition for browsing on higher branches must be between giraffe and giraffe, and not with other animals.

Insects often resemble for the sake of protection various objects. Mr. Mivart remarks, "As incipient variations will be in *all directions,* they must tend to neutralize each other, and it is difficult to see how such indefinite oscillations of infinitesimal beginnings can ever build up a sufficient resemblance for Natural Selection to seize upon and perpetuate." But the insects in their original state no doubt presented some rude resemblance to an object commonly found in the stations frequented by them. Nor is this at all improbable, considering the almost infinite number of surrounding objects. Assuming that an insect originally happened to resemble in some degree a dead twig or a decayed leaf, then all the variations which rendered the insect more like, and thus favoured its escape, would be preserved, whilst other variations would be neglected. There would be force in Mr. Mivart's objection, if we were to attempt to account for the above resemblances through mere fluctuating variability; but as the case stands there is none.

Flat-fish are remarkable for their asymmetrical bodies. They rest on one side. That they are admirably adapted for their habits of life, is manifest from several species, such as soles, flounders, &c., being extremely common. Their chief advantages seem to be protection from enemies and facility for feeding on the ground. Their lower surface is white, less developed than the upper, with the lateral fins often of smaller size. But the eyes offer the most remarkable peculiarity; for they are both on the upper side of the head. During early youth, however, they stand opposite to each other, and the whole body is symmetrical, with both sides equally coloured. Soon the eye on the lower side begins to glide slowly round the head. Unless it did, it could not be used by the fish whilst lying in its habitual position on one side, and would also be liable to be abraded by the sandy bottom.

Mr. Mivart remarks, "if the transit was gradual, then how such transit of one eye a minute fraction towards the other side of the head could benefit the individual is far from clear. It must rather have been injurious." But he might have found an answer in the excellent observations published in 1867 by Malm. The very young and still symmetrical Flat-fish cannot long retain a vertical position, owing to the excessive depth of their bodies, their small lateral fins, and their lack of a swim-bladder. Soon growing tired, they fall to the bottom on one side. Thus at rest they often twist the lower eye upwards, to see above them, so vigorously that the eye is pressed hard against the upper part of the orbit. The forehead consequently becomes, as can be plainly seen, temporarily contracted in breadth. The skull at this early age is flexible and readily yields to muscular action. The older the fish grow the more habitually they rest on one side, owing to the increasing flatness of their bodies, and a permanent effect is thus produced on the form of the head, and on the position of the eyes. The tendency to distortion would no doubt be increased through inheritance.

Disuse also accounts for the less developed condition of the whole inferior half of the body. As I have before insisted, the inherited effects of the increased use of parts, and perhaps of their disuse, will be strengthened by natural selection.

In the vegetable kingdom Mr. Mivart alludes to the movements of climbing plants. Climbing plants can be arranged in a series, from those which twine, to leaf-climbers and those provided with tendrils. From simple twiners to leaf-climbers, an important quality is added, sensitiveness to a touch, by which means the foot-stalks or tendrils are excited to bend round and clasp the touching object. It is clearly a great advantage, and it is probable that every twiner which possessed leaves with long foot-stalks would have been developed into a leaf-climber, if the foot-stalks had possessed in any slight degree the requisite sensitiveness to a touch.

As twining is the simplest means of ascending a support, how did plants acquire this power in an incipient degree? The power depends on the stem whilst young being extremely flexible and on their continually bending to all points of the compass in the same order. When the lower part of a stem strikes against any object and is stopped, the upper part goes on revolving, and thus necessarily twines round the support. I was led to predict that some slight tendency to a movement of this kind would be found to be far from uncommon with plants which did not climb. I knew of only one imperfect case. Soon afterwards, Fritz Müller discovered that the young stems of an Alisma and of a Linum revolved plainly, though irregularly; and he suspects that this occurs with some other plants. If under the conditions to which they are exposed it had profited these plants to ascend to a height, the habit of slightly and irregularly revolving might have been increased through natural selection, until they had become converted into twining species.

With respect to foot-stalks and tendrils, nearly the same remarks are applicable. I observed that the young flower-peduncles of Maurandia curved themselves a little towards the side which was touched. Morren found in several species of Oxalis that leaves and foot-stalks moved, especially after exposure to a hot sun, when gently and repeatedly touched, or when the plant was shaken. According to the high authority of Hofmeister, young shoots and leaves of all plants move after being shaken.

Plants possess powers of movement, manifestly important to them; for instance, towards light, or in opposition to gravity. From having the power of movement in obedience to certain stimuli, they are excited in an incidental manner by a touch, or by being shaken. Hence there is no great difficulty in admitting it is this tendency which has been taken advantage of and increased through natural selection.

Arguments from natural selection and embryology indicate that species were not formed by abrupt changes

Mr. Mivart is inclined to believe, and some naturalists agree, that new species manifest themselves "with suddenness and by modifications appearing at once." For instance, he thinks it difficult to believe that the wing of a bird "was developed in any other way than by a comparatively sudden modification of a marked and important kind."

As species are more variable when domesticated than under nature, it is not probable that such abrupt variations have often occurred under nature, as are known occasionally under domestication. Abrupt and strongly marked variations occur in our domesticated productions, singly and at rather long intervals of time. If such occurred under nature, they would be liable to be lost by accidental causes and by inter-crossing. In order that a new species should suddenly appear, it is almost necessary to believe, in opposition to all analogy, that several wonderfully changed individuals appeared simultaneously within the same district.

Against the belief in abrupt changes, embryology enters a strong protest. The embryo serves as a record of the past condition of the species. Hence existing species during early stages often resemble extinct forms belonging to the same class. It is incredible that an animal should have undergone abrupt transformations and yet should not bear even a trace in its embryonic condition of sudden modification, every detail being developed by insensibly fine steps.

He who believes that some ancient form was transformed suddenly through an internal force or tendency will be compelled to believe that many structures beautifully adapted to all the other parts of the same creature and to the surrounding conditions, have been suddenly produced; and of such complex and wonderful co-adaptations, he will not be able to assign a shadow of an explanation.

CHAPTER VIII

Instinct

Like habits, instincts are rhythmic and inflexible; unlike habits, they are always inherited

Many instincts are so wonderful that their development will probably appear to the reader a difficulty sufficient to overthrow my whole theory. Everyone understands what is meant by instinct. An action, which we require experience to enable us to perform, when performed by an animal, without experience, and when performed by many individuals in the same way, without their knowing for what purpose it is performed, is usually said to be instinctive. None of these characters is universal. A little dose of judgment or reason often comes into play.

Resemblances between instincts and habits could be pointed out. As in repeating a well-known song, so in instincts, one action follows another by a sort of rhythm; if a person be interrupted in a song he is generally forced to go back to recover the habitual train of thought; so P. Huber found if he took a caterpillar which had completed its hammock up to the sixth stage of construction, and put it into a hammock completed only to the third stage, the caterpillar simply re-performed the fourth, fifth and sixth stages of construction. If, however, a caterpillar were taken out of a hammock made up to the third stage, and put into one finished up to the sixth, it was much embarrassed, seemed forced to start from where it had left off, and thus tried to complete the already finished work.

If we suppose any habitual action to become inherited—and this does sometimes happen—then the resemblance between what originally was a habit and an instinct becomes extremely close. But it would be a serious error to suppose that the greater number of instincts have been acquired by habit in one generation and then transmitted by inheritance to succeeding generations. It can be clearly shown that the most wonderful instincts with which we are acquainted, namely, those of the hive-bee and of many ants, could not possibly have been acquired by habit.

Being heritable, variable, and useful, instincts are, like physical characters, subject to natural selection

It will be universally admitted that instincts are as important as corporeal structures for the welfare of each species. If it can be shown that instincts vary ever so little, I see no difficulty in natural selection preserving and continually accumulating variations of instinct to any extent that was profitable. I have been surprised to find how very generally gradations leading to the most complex instincts can be discovered. It is thus, as I believe, that all the most complex and wonderful instincts have originated. I believe that the effects of habit are of subordinate importance to the effects of the natural selection of what may be called spontaneous variations of instincts.

As with corporeal structure, the instinct of each species has never been produced for the exclusive good of others. One of the strongest instances of an animal apparently performing an action for the good of another is that of aphides yielding their sweet excretion to ants. I removed all the ants from a group of about a dozen aphides during several hours. After this interval, I felt sure that the aphides would want to excrete. I watched them for some time through a lens, but not one excreted. Afterwards I allowed an ant to visit them; it began to play with its antennae on the abdomen first of one aphis and then of another; and each excreted a limpid drop of sweet juice, which was eagerly devoured by the ant. Even the quite young aphides behaved in this manner, showing that the action was instinctive, and not the result of experience. If ants be not present, aphides are at last compelled to eject their excretion. But as it is extremely viscid, it is no doubt a convenience to the aphides to have it removed.

Instincts certainly vary—for instance, the migratory instinct, both in extent and direction, and in its total loss. Audubon gives cases of differences in the nests of same species in the northern and southern United States. Several cases could also be adduced of occasional and strange habits in wild animals, which, if advantageous to the species, might have given rise, through natural selection, to new instincts. I am well aware that these general statements will produce but a feeble effect on the reader's mind. I can only repeat that I do not speak without good evidence.

It is notorious how much domestic animals vary in their mental qualities. One cat naturally takes to catching rats, and another mice, and these tendencies are known to be inherited. Young pointers will sometimes point the first time they are taken out; retrieving is inherited by retrievers; and a tendency to run round, instead of at, a flock of sheep, by shepherd dogs. I cannot see that these actions, performed with eager delight by each breed, and without the end being known, differ essentially from true instincts.

No one would ever have thought of teaching the tumbler-pigeon to tumble—an action performed by young birds that have never seen a pigeon tumble. We may believe that one pigeon showed a tendency to this strange habit and that selection of the best individuals in successive generations made tumblers what they now are. Pointing is probably the exaggerated pause of an animal preparing to spring on its prey. The tendency to point once displayed, selection and the inherited effects of training in each generation would soon complete the work. Habit alone in some cases has sufficed; hardly any animal is more difficult to tame than the young of the wild rabbit; scarcely any animal is tamer than the young of the tame rabbit.

Natural instincts are lost under domestication: a remarkable instance of this is seen in those breeds of fowls which never wish to sit on their eggs. How rarely do dogs even when young require to be taught not to attack poultry, sheep, and pigs! They occasionally do make an attack and are beaten; if not cured, they are destroyed; so that habit and some selection have concurred in civilizing by inheritance our dogs. On the other hand, young chickens have lost, wholly by habit, their original instinctive fear of the dog and cat.

The graded instincts of various species of the cuckoo and the ant illustrate how an elaborate instinct may develop

The cuckoo lays her eggs at intervals of two or three days; so that, if she were to make her own nest and sit on her own eggs there would be eggs and young birds of different ages in the same nest. The process of laying and hatching might be inconveniently long, especially as she migrates very early; and the first hatched would probably have to be fed by the male alone. The American cuckoo is in this predicament, for she makes her own nest and has eggs successively hatched. But Mr. Merrell, of Iowa, once found a young cuckoo together with a young jay in the nest of a blue jay. Let us suppose that the ancient progenitor of our European cuckoo had the habits of the American cuckoo but that she occasionally laid an egg in another bird's nest. If she profited by this occasional habit through being enabled to migrate earlier or if the young were made more vigorous than when reared by their own mother, then the old birds or the fostered young would gain an advantage. The young thus reared would be apt to follow by inheritance the occasional habit of their mother. By a continued process of this nature, I believe that the strange instinct of our cuckoo has been generated.

The chief points are three: first, the common cuckoo, with rare exceptions, lays only one egg in a nest, so that the large and voracious young bird receives ample food. Secondly, the eggs are remarkably small; that this is a case of adaptation we may infer from the fact of the non-parasitic American cuckoo laying full-sized eggs. Thirdly, the young, soon after birth, has the instinct, the strength, and a properly shaped back for ejecting its foster-brothers, which then perish from cold and hunger. In the Australian Bronze cuckoo eggs vary greatly in size. Now if it had been an advantage to this species to have laid smaller eggs, there is no difficulty in believing that a species might have been formed which would have laid smaller and smaller eggs. The European cuckoo commonly ejects the offspring of the foster-parents from the nest within three days after being hatched. A young cuckoo was actually seen, still blind and not able even to hold up its head, in the act of ejecting its foster-brothers. One was replaced by the observer, and was again thrown out. As to how this odious instinct was acquired, if it were of great importance for the young cuckoo, as is probably the case, to receive much food soon after birth, I can see no difficulty in its having acquired, during successive generations, the blind desire, the strength, and structure necessary for the work of ejection. The first step might have been mere restlessness on the part of the young bird, the habit having been afterwards improved, and transmitted to an earlier age.

Many bees are parasitic, and regularly lay their eggs in the nests of other kinds of bees. This case is more remarkable than that of the cuckoo, for these bees have also had their structure modified; they do not possess the pollen-collecting apparatus indispensable if they stored up food for their own young.

The slave-making instinct was first discovered in the Formica rufescens by Pierre Huber. This ant is absolutely dependent on its slaves; without their aid, the species would become extinct in a year. The males and fertile females do no work and the workers, though most courageous in capturing slaves, do no other work. They are incapable of making their own nests or of feeding their own larvae. When they have to migrate, it is the slaves which determine the migration and actually carry their masters in their jaws. When Huber shut up thirty of them without a slave but with plenty of food, they could not even feed themselves and many perished. Huber then introduced a single slave and she instantly set to work, fed and saved the survivors; made cells, tended the larvae, and put all to rights. What can be more extraordinary than these well-ascertained facts? If we had known of no other slave-making ant, it would have been hopeless to speculate how so wonderful an instinct could have been perfected.

Another species, Formica sanguinea, was likewise first discovered by P. Huber to be a slave-making ant. I tried to approach the subject in a sceptical frame of mind. I opened fourteen nests of F. sanguinea, and found a few slaves in all. The contrast in their appearance is great. When the nest is disturbed, and the larvae and pupae are exposed, the slaves work energetically together with their masters in carrying them away to a place of safety. Hence, it is clear that the slaves feel quite at home. I watched for many hours several nests and never saw a slave either leave or enter a nest, though the masters may be constantly seen bringing in materials and food for the nest. According to Huber, the slaves in Switzerland habitually work with their masters in making the nest; they open and close the doors morning and evening; and their principal office is to search for aphides. This difference in habits in the two countries probably depends on the slaves being captured in greater numbers in Switzerland than here.

One day I fortunately witnessed a migration of F. sanguinea; it was most interesting to behold the masters carefully carrying their slaves in their jaws instead of being carried by them, as in the case of F. rufescens. Another day my attention was struck by about a score of the slave-makers haunting the same spot, and evidently not in search of food; they approached and were vigorously repulsed by a community of the slave species. They ruthlessly killed their small opponents and carried their dead bodies as food to their nest, twenty-nine yards distant; but they were prevented from getting any pupae to rear as slaves. I then dug up a small parcel of pupae from another nest and put them near the place of combat; they were eagerly seized and carried off by the tyrants, who perhaps fancied that, after all, they had been victorious in their late combat.

At the same time I laid on the same place a small parcel of the pupae of another species, F. flava, with a few of these little yellow ants still clinging to the fragments of their nest. This species is sometimes, though rarely, made into slaves. I was curious to ascertain whether F. sanguinea could distinguish the pupae of the little and furious F. flava. They were terrified when they came across the pupae, or even the earth from the nest of F. flava, and quickly ran away; but in about a quarter of an hour, shortly after all the little yellow ants had crawled away, they took heart and carried off the pupae.

By what steps the instinct of F. sanguinea originated I will not pretend to conjecture. It is possible that pupae originally stored as food by ants which were not slave-makers might become developed; and the foreign ants thus unintentionally reared would then follow their proper instincts, and do what work they could. The habit of collecting pupae, originally for food, might by natural

selection be strengthened and rendered permanent for the
very different purpose of raising slaves, until an ant was
formed as abjectly dependent on its slaves as is the Formica rufescens.

*The structures and instincts
of neuter females can be explained on the theory that
communities as well as individuals can be selected*

No doubt many instincts
are very difficult to explain
by natural selection. I will
confine myself to one
special difficulty which at
first appeared to me in-
superable.   I allude to the neuters or sterile females in
insect-communities; they differ widely in instinct and in
structure from both the males and fertile females, and
yet, from being sterile, they cannot propagate their kind.
How is it possible to reconcile this case with the theory of
natural selection?

First, we have innumerable instances of all sorts of
differences of inherited structure which are correlated with
certain ages and with either sex. We have even slight
differences in the horns of different breeds of cattle in
relation to an artificially imperfect state of the male sex.
The difficulty lies in understanding how such correlated
modifications could have been slowly accumulated by natural selection.

This difficulty as I believe disappears when it is remembered that selection may be applied to the family as
well as to the individual. Some varieties of the double
Stock, from having been selected to the right degree, produce a large proportion of seedlings bearing double and
quite sterile flowers; but they likewise yield some single
and fertile plants. These may be compared with the fertile male and female ants, and the double sterile plants
with the neuter ants. Hence we may conclude that slight
modifications of structure or of instinct, correlated with
the sterility of certain members of the community, have
proved advantageous to all: consequently the fertile

males and females have flourished, and transmitted to their fertile offspring a tendency to produce sterile members with the same modifications. This process must have been repeated until that prodigious amount of difference between the fertile and sterile females has been produced, which we see in many social insects.

But we have not yet touched on the acme of the difficulty: the fact that the neuters differ, not only from the fertile females and males, but from each other, sometimes to an almost incredible degree, and are thus divided into two or even three castes as distinct from each other as any two genera of the same family. There are working and soldier neuters, with jaws and instincts extraordinarily different: in a Mexican species the workers of one caste never leave the nest; they are fed by the workers of another caste, and they have an enormously developed abdomen which secretes a sort of honey, supplying the place of that excreted by aphides.

In the simpler case of neuter insects all of one caste we may conclude that profitable modifications did not first arise in all the neuters in the same nest, and that by the survival of the communities with females which produced most neuters having the advantageous modification, all the neuters ultimately came to be thus characterised. According to this view we ought occasionally to find in the same nest neuter insects, presenting gradations of structure. And the neuters of several British ants differ surprisingly from each other in size and sometimes in colour; the extreme forms can be linked together by individuals from the same nest.

I gladly availed myself of Mr. F. Smith's offer of numerous specimens from the same nest of the driver ant of West Africa. The difference in these workers was the same as if we were to see a set of workmen building a house, of whom many were five feet four inches high, and many sixteen feet high. But the important fact is that, though the workers can be grouped into castes of different sizes, yet they graduate insensibly into each other, as does the widely-different structure of their jaws.

I believe that natural selection could form a species which should regularly produce neuters, all of large size with one form of jaw, or all of small size with widely different jaws; or simultaneously two sets of workers of a different size and structure—the extreme forms having been produced in greater and greater numbers, through the survival of the parents which generated them, until none with an intermediate structure were produced.

We can see how useful their production may have been to a community of ants, on the same principle that the division of labour is useful to man. I have discussed this case in order to show the power of natural selection, and because this is by far the most serious special difficulty which my theory has encountered. The case, also, proves that any amount of modification may be effected without exercise of habit having been brought into play. Habits confined to the workers or sterile females could not possibly affect the males and fertile females, which alone leave descendants. I am surprised that no one has hitherto advanced this demonstrative case of neuter insects, against the well-known doctrine of inherited habit, as advanced by Lamarck.

My theory is also strengthened by some few other facts in regard to instincts; as by that common case of closely allied species inhabiting distant parts of the world and living under considerably different conditions of life often retaining nearly the same instincts. For instance, we can understand, on the principle of inheritance, how it is that the Hornbills of Africa and India have the same extraordinary instinct of plastering up and imprisoning the females in a hole in a tree, with only a small hole left in the plaster through which the males feed them and their young when hatched.

Finally, it may not be a logical deduction, but to my imagination it is far more satisfactory to look at such instincts as the young cuckoo ejecting its foster-brothers—ants making slaves—not as specially endowed or created instincts, but as small consequences of one general law leading to the advancement of all organic beings—namely, multiply, vary, let the strongest live and the weakest die.

CHAPTER IX

Hybridism

Sterility is not universal when species are crossed; its appearance is often due to incidental factors, such as inbreeding

The view commonly entertained by naturalists is that species, when intercrossed, have been specially endowed with sterility, in order to prevent their confusion. The subject is in many ways important for us, especially as the sterility of species when first crossed, and that of their hybrid offspring, cannot have been acquired, as I shall show, by the preservation of profitable degrees of sterility. It is an incidental result of differences in the reproductive systems of the parent-species.

In this subject, two classes of facts, fundamentally different, have generally been confounded: the sterility of species when first crossed, and the sterility of the hybrids produced from them.

Pure species have of course their organs of reproduction in a perfect condition, yet when intercrossed they produce either few or no offspring. Hybrids, on the other hand, have their reproductive organs functionally impotent, though perfect in structure. This distinction is important. The fertility of varieties, that is of the forms descended from common parents, when crossed, and likewise the fertility of their mongrel offspring, is with reference to my theory, of equal importance with the sterility of species; for it seems to make a broad and clear distinction between varieties and species.

The sterility of various species when crossed is so different and graduates so insensibly, and the fertility of pure species is so easily affected by various circumstances, that it is most difficult to say where perfect fertility ends and sterility begins.

In regard to the sterility of hybrids in successive generations: though Gaertner was enabled to rear some hybrids, carefully guarding them from a cross with either pure parent, for six or seven, and in one case ten generations, he asserts positively that fertility never increases, but generally decreases greatly and suddenly. With respect to this decrease, when any deviation is common to both parents, this is often transmitted in an augmented degree to the offspring; and both sexual elements in hybrid plants are already affected in some degree. But I believe that their fertility has been diminished by an independent cause—by too close interbreeding. Hybrids are seldom raised by experimentalists in great numbers; and as the parent-species or other hybrids generally grow in the same garden, the visits of insects are carefully prevented during the flowering season. Hence they will generally be fertilised by pollen from the same flower; and this would be injurious to their fertility, already lessened by their hybrid origin. I am strengthened in this conviction by a statement repeatedly made by Gaertner, that if even the less fertile hybrids be artifically fertilised, their fertility, notwithstanding the ill effects from manipulation, sometimes decidedly increases and goes on increasing. Now, in the process of artificial fertilisation, pollen is often taken by chance (as I know from my own experience) from the anthers of another flower. Moreover, so careful an observer as Gaertner would have castrated his hybrids, and this would have ensured a cross with a distinct flower. Thus, the increase of fertility in the successive generations of *artificially fertilised* hybrids may be accounted for by too close interbreeding having been avoided.

Another most experienced hybridiser, the Rev. W. Herbert, is as emphatic in his conclusion that some hybrids are perfectly fertile, as is Gaertner that some degree of sterility is a universal law of nature. The difference may be in part accounted for by Herbert's great horticultural skill, and by his having hot-houses at his command. It is notorious in how complicated a manner the species of Pelargonium, Fuchsia, Petunia, Rhododendron, etc., have been crossed, yet many of these hybrids seed freely. Had hybrids when fairly treated always gone on decreasing in fertility in each successive generation, the fact would have been notorious to nursery men. But horticulturists raise large beds of the same hybrid so that by insect agency individuals are allowed to cross freely and the injurious influence of close interbreeding is thus prevented.

In regard to animals, fewer experiments have been tried. We may infer that animals more widely distinct can be crossed more easily than plants; but the hybrids themselves are more sterile. However, I hardly know of an instance in which two families of the same hybrid have been raised from different parents, so as to avoid the ill effects of interbreeding: brothers and sisters have usually been crossed in each generation, in opposition to the constantly repeated admonition of every breeder. The hybrids from two moths were fertile *inter se* for eight generations. It has lately been asserted that two such distinct species as the hare and rabbit, when they can be got to breed together, produce offspring, which are highly fertile when crossed with one of the parent-species.

With our domesticated animals, the various races when crossed together are quite fertile; yet in many cases they are descended from two or more wild species. For instance, our dogs are descended from several wild stocks; yet all are quite fertile together; but analogy makes me greatly doubt, whether the several aboriginal species would at first have freely bred together and produced fertile hybrids. The Indian humped and common cattle are *inter se* perfectly fertile. The same remarks may be extended to the two chief races of the pig. We must therefore either give up the belief of the universal sterility of species when crossed; or we must look at this sterility, not as indelible, but as capable of being removed by domestication. Finally, it may be concluded that some degree of sterility, both in first crosses and hybrids, is an extremely general result; but it cannot, with our present knowledge, be considered as absolutely universal.

Sterility in crossed species varies widely, depending on unknown differences in their reproductive systems

Our chief object will be to see whether the laws governing the sterility of first crosses and hybrids indicate that species have been endowed with sterility to prevent their blending together in utter confusion. The following conclusions are drawn up chiefly from Gaertner's admirable work on the hybridisation of plants. And, considering how scanty our knowledge is in regard to hybrid animals, I have been surprised to find how generally the same rules apply to both kingdoms.

When pollen from a plant of one family is placed on the stigma of a plant of a distinct family, it exerts no more influence than so much inorganic dust. From this absolute zero of fertility, the pollen of different species applied to the stigma of some one species of the same genus yields a perfect gradation in the number of seeds produced, up to complete fertility. So in hybrids themselves, there are some which never have produced a single fertile seed: but in some of these the pollen of one of the parent-species may cause the flower to wither earlier—a well known sign of incipient fertilisation. From this extreme degree of sterility we have self-fertilised hybrids producing a greater number of seeds up to perfect fertility.

Hybrids raised from two species which are very difficult to cross are generally very sterile, but the parallelism is by no means strict. There are many cases in which two species can be united with facility and produce numerous hybrid-offspring, yet these hybrids are remarkably sterile. On the other hand, there are species which can be crossed very rarely, but the hybrids, when at last produced, are very fertile. The fertility of first crosses and of hybrids is more easily affected by unfavourable conditions than is that of pure species. But the fertility of first crosses is likewise innately variable, and with hybrids it often differs greatly in individuals raised from seed out of the same capsule and exposed to the same conditions.

Systematic affinity means the general resemblance between species in structure and constitution. Now fertility is largely governed by systematic affinity. This is shown by hybrids never having been raised between distinct families, and by closely allied species generally uniting with facility. But the correspondence between systematic affinity and the facility of crossing is by no means strict. Even in the same family there may be a genus in which very many species can readily be crossed; and another genus in which the most persevering efforts have failed to produce between extremely close species a single hybrid. Plants having strongly marked differences in every part can be crossed. Annual and perennial plants, deciduous and evergreen trees, plants fitted for extremely different climates, can often be crossed with ease.

A reciprocal cross between two species is that, for instance, of a female-ass with a stallion, and then that of a mare with a male-ass. There is often the widest possible difference in the facility of making reciprocal crosses. Such cases are highly important, for they prove that the capacity to cross is often completely independent of systematic affinity—that is, of any difference in structure or constitution, excepting in reproductive systems. It is also remarkable that hybrids from reciprocal crosses, though rarely differing externally, generally differ in fertility in a small, and occasionally in a high degree.

Do these singular rules indicate that species have been endowed with sterility to prevent their becoming confounded? I think not. For why should the sterility be so extremely different in degree? Why should it vary in individuals of the same species? Why should some species cross with facility, and produce sterile hybrids; and other species cross with extreme difficulty, and produce fairly fertile hybrids? Why should there often be so great a difference in the result of reciprocal crosses? Why, it may even be asked, has the production of hybrids been permitted?

The facts indicate that sterility is simply incidental or dependent on unknown differences in reproductive systems; the differences being so limited, that the male sexual element of one species will often freely act on the female sexual element of the other, but not in the reversed direction. There must sometimes be a physical impossibility in the male element reaching the ovule. It may reach the female element but be incapable of causing an embryo to be developed. Lastly, an embryo may be developed and perish at an early period. Mr. Salter has examined about 500 eggs from various crosses; the majority had been fertilised; and in the majority of the fertilised eggs, the embryos were either partially developed or nearly mature, but the young chickens had been unable to break through the shell. Of the chickens which were born, more than four-fifths died within the first few days or weeks. From the 500 eggs only twelve chickens were reared. With plants, hybrids raised from very distinct species are sometimes weak and dwarfed, and perish early. A hybrid partakes of only half of the nature and constitution of its mother; it may therefore before birth or within the egg or seed be exposed to unsuitable conditions. But after all, the cause probably lies in some imperfection in the original act of impregnation, causing an imperfect embryo to develop.

Unnatural conditions affect fertility, and with hybrids, blending two organisms into one has the same effect

In regard to the sterility of hybrids, in which the sexual elements are imperfect, the case is somewhat different. I have alluded to a body of facts showing that animals and plants removed from their natural conditions are extremely liable to have their reproductive systems affected. Between such sterility and that of hybrids, there are many points of similarity: the sterility is independent of general health and is often accompanied by great luxuriance. In both cases the male element is the most liable to be affected. Lastly, when beings are placed during several generations under unnatural conditions, they are eminently liable to vary, partly due to their reproductive systems having been specially affected. So are hybrids eminently liable to vary. With them, external conditions remain the same, but the organisation has been disturbed by two distinct structures, including of course the reproductive systems, having been blended into one. When hybrids breed *inter se,* they transmit to their offspring from generation to generation the same compounded organisation, and hence their sterility does not diminish.

It must, however, be owned that we cannot understand, on the above or any other view, several facts: for instance, the unequal fertility of hybrids produced from reciprocal crosses. Nor do I pretend to go to the root of the matter; no explanation is offered why an organism, under unnatural conditions, is rendered sterile. All I have attempted to show is, that in two allied cases, sterility is the common result.

A similar parallelism holds good with an allied yet very different class of facts. It is an universal belief founded on considerable evidence that slight changes in the conditions of life are beneficial to all living things. Again, there is the clearest evidence that a cross between individuals of the same species, which differ to a certain extent, gives vigour and fertility to the offspring; and that close interbreeding almost always leads to decreased size, weakness, or sterility.

But beings subjected to considerable change are rendered more or less sterile; and a cross between two forms widely different, produces hybrids almost always in some degree sterile. These two parallel series of facts seem to be connected by some unknown bond, which is essentially related to the principle of life.

Fertility does not constitute a fundamental distinction between varieties and species when crossed

It may be urged that there must be some essential distinction between species and varieties, as the latter cross easily and yield fertile offspring. But if two forms reputed to be varieties be found sterile together, they are at once ranked by most naturalists as species. If we thus argue in a circle, the fertility of all varieties will assuredly have to be granted.

With wild species the cause of sterility lies exclusively in differences in their sexual constitution. But we have good grounds for admitting the doctrine of Pallas, that conditions of domestication generally eliminate the tendency toward sterility; so that domesticated descendants of species, which in their natural state probably would have been sterile when crossed, become fertile together.

The real difficulty is why natural varieties have so generally become mutually infertile, as soon as they have been modified sufficiently to rank as species. Species, owing to their struggle for existence, will have been exposed during long periods of time to more uniform conditions than have domestic varieties; and this may well make a wide difference. For we know how commonly wild animals and plants, when taken from their natural conditions, are rendered sterile; and the reproductive functions of such beings would probably likewise be sensitive to the influence of an unnatural cross. Domesticated productions which, as shown by their domestication, were not highly sensitive to changes in their conditions, might be expected to produce varieties, which would be little liable to have their reproductive powers injured by crossing with other varieties which had originated in a like manner.

I have as yet spoken as if varieties of the same species were invariably fertile when intercrossed, but evidence can be produced, even from hostile witnesses, that varieties when crossed are not invariably quite fertile. Thus, the general sterility of crossed species may safely be looked at as not a special endowment. In all other respects there seems to be a general and close similarity in the offspring of crossed species, and of crossed varieties. If we look at species as having been specially created, and at varieties as having been produced by secondary laws, this similarity would be an astonishing fact. But it harmonises perfectly with the view that there is no essential distinction between species and varieties.

CHAPTER X

On the Imperfections of the Geological Record

Fossil forms will be intermediate, not between existing species, but between them and a common ancestor

I have found it difficult, when looking at any two species, to avoid picturing to myself forms *directly* intermediate between them. But this is a wholly false view; we should always look for forms intermediate between each species and a common but unknown progenitor; and the progenitor will generally have differed in some respects from all its modified descendants. The fantail and pouter pigeons are both descended from the rock-pigeon; if we possessed all the intermediate varieties, we should have a close series between both and the rock-pigeon; but we should have no varieties combining a tail somewhat expanded with a crop somewhat enlarged, the characteristic features of these two breeds. Moreover, in all such cases we should be unable to recognise the parent-form even if we closely compared its structure with that of its modified descendants, unless we had a nearly perfect chain of the intermediate links.

It is just possible that one form might have descended from the other; for instance, a horse from a tapir; in this case *direct* intermediate links will have existed between them. But the principle of competition between child and parent will render this a rare event.

Ample time has elapsed for infinite gradations of change

By the theory of natural selection the number of intermediate and transitional links, between all living and extinct species, must have been inconceivably great. Independently of our not finding fossil remains of such connecting links, it may be objected that time cannot have sufficed for such great change, all changes having been slow. We can best gain some idea of the immensity of past time by knowing the agencies at work.

It is good to wander along the coast and mark the process of degradation. The tides reach the cliffs only a short time twice a day, and the waves eat into them only when charged with sand or pebbles. At last the base of the cliff is undermined, huge fragments fall down and have to be worn away atom by atom, until they can be rolled about by the waves; then they are more quickly ground up. But how often do we see boulders, thickly clothed with marine productions, showing how little they are abraded and how seldom they are rolled about! Moreover, it is only here and there, along a short length, that the cliffs are at the present time suffering.

Yet subaerial degradation is a much more important agency than the waves. The whole surface of the land is exposed to the chemical action of the air and of rain-water with its carbonic acid, and in colder countries to frost; the disintegrated matter is carried down slopes during rain, and in arid districts by the wind; it is then transported by streams and rivers. The great lines of escarpment ranging across England owe their origin to having resisted subaerial denudation better than the surrounding surface. Nothing impresses the mind with the vast duration of time more forcibly than that subaerial agencies which apparently have so little power and which work so slowly, have produced great results.

But let it be borne in mind what a hundred years implies. Breeders, during a single lifetime, have so largely modified some of the higher animals, which propagate their kind slowly, that they have formed a new sub-breed. By unconscious selection, various breeds have been sensibly changed in the course of two or three centuries. Species, however, probably change much more slowly, and only a few at a time. New places in the polity of nature do not occur until after long intervals, due to the occurrence of physical changes of some kind, or through the immigration of new forms.

But geological conditions necessary to preserve rich fossil beds occur only rarely and intermittently. So that geology does not reveal fine gradations

Now let us turn to our richest geological museums, and what a paltry display we behold! Many fossil species are known and famed from single and often broken specimens collected on one spot. Only a small portion of the surface of the earth has been geologically explored, and no part with sufficient care. No organism wholly soft can be preserved. Shells and bones decay and disappear when left where sediment is not accumulating. The remains which do become embedded will, when the beds are upraised, generally be dissolved by rain-water charged with carbolic acid. Lastly, many great deposits requiring a vast length of time for their accumulation are entirely destitute of organic remains without our being able to assign any reason.

But the imperfection in the record largely results from a more important cause—from the several formations being separated from each other by wide intervals of time. This doctrine has been emphatically admitted by many geologists and palaeontologists who entirely disbelieve in the change of species.

Sediment must be accumulated in thick, solid, or extensive masses, to withstand the incessant action of the waves, when first upraised and during successive oscillations of level, as well as the subsequent subaerial degradation. Such accumulations may be formed; either in profound depths of the sea, in which case the bottom will not be inhabited by such varied forms of life, or by deposits of sediment to any thickness and extent over a shallow bottom, if it continue slowly to subside. As long as the rate of subsidence and the supply of sediment nearly balance each other, the sea will remain shallow and favourable for many and varied forms, and a rich fossiliferous formation, thick enough, when upraised, to resist a large amount of denudation, may be formed. I am convinced that nearly all our ancient formations, which are *rich in fossils,* have thus been formed.

One remark is here worth a passing notice. During periods of elevation the area of the land and of the shoal parts of the sea will be increased—circumstances favourable for the formation of new varieties and species; but during such periods there will generally be a blank in the geological record. During subsidence, the inhabited area and inhabitants will decrease, and few new species will be formed; it is during these very periods that the deposits richest in fossils have been accumulated.

If we confine our attention to any one formation, it becomes much more difficult to understand why we do not find closely graduated varieties between the allied species which lived at its commencement and at its close. With marine animals of all kinds there has been a large amount of migration. When a species first appears in any formation, the probability is that it only then immigrated into that area. For instance, several species appear somewhat earlier in the palaeozoic beds of North America than in those of Europe.

Again, it would seem that each formation has been intermittent in its accumulation. Many instances could be given of beds only a few feet thick, representing formations, which are elsewhere thousands of feet thick; yet no one would have suspected the vast lapse of time represented by the thinner formation. Hence, when the same species occurs at the bottom, middle, and top of a formation, the probability is that it has not lived on the same spot, but has disappeared and reappeared, perhaps many times during the same geological period. Consequently, a section would not include all the fine gradations, but abrupt, though perhaps slight, changes; so that we might obtain the parent-species and its several modified descendants from the lower and upper beds of the same formation, and unless we obtained transitional gradations, not recognise their relationship, and rank them as distinct species. Again, it is important that the period during which each species underwent modification, though long in years, was probably short in comparison with that during which it remained without change.

The abrupt appearance of some whole groups of species indicates rather the imperfection of the geological record than sudden creation

If numerous species have really started into life at once, the fact would be fatal to the theory of natural selection. But we falsely infer, because certain genera or families have not been found beneath a certain stage, that they did not exist before that stage. In all cases positive palaeontological evidence may be implicitly trusted; negative evidence is worthless, as experience has so often shown. I will give a few examples. In geological treatises, not many years ago, mammals were always spoken of as having abruptly come in at the commencement of the tertiary series. And now one of the richest known accumulations of fossil mammals belongs to the middle of the secondary series; and true mammals have been discovered in the new red sandstone at nearly the commencement of this series. Cuvier used to urge that no monkey occurred in any tertiary stratum; but now extinct species have been discovered as far back as the Miocene stage. Had it not been for the rare accident of the preservation of footsteps in the new red sandstone of the United States, who would have supposed that at least thirty bird-like animals existed during that period?

An allied difficulty is much more serious: species belonging to several of the main divisions of the animal kingdom suddenly appear in the lowest known fossiliferous rocks. Consequently, if the theory be true, it is indisputable that before the lowest Cambrian stratum was deposited periods elapsed as long as, or probably far longer than, the whole interval from the Cambrian age to the present day; and that during these vast periods the world swarmed with living creatures.

The difficulty of assigning any good reason for the absence of strata rich in fossils beneath the Cambrian system is very great. The case at present may be truly urged as a valid argument against my views. To show that it may hereafter receive some explanation, I will give the following hypothesis. If we may infer anything we may infer that, where our oceans now extend, oceans have extended from the remotest period of which we have any record; where continents now exist, large tracts of land have existed, subjected no doubt to great oscillations of level, since the Cambrian period. The great oceans are still mainly areas of subsidence, the great archipelagos still areas of oscillations of level, and the continents, areas of elevation. But at a period long antecedent to the Cambrian epoch, continents may have existed where oceans now are; and oceans may have existed where our continents stand. It might well happen that strata which had subsided near the centre of the earth, and which had been pressed on by an enormous weight of water, might have undergone far more metamorphic action than strata nearer the surface. The immense areas in South America of naked metamorphic rocks, which must have been heated under great pressure, have always seemed to me to require some special explanation; and perhaps we see in these, the many formations long anterior to the Cambrian epoch.

The difficulties are undoubtedly serious. Eminent palaeontologists and all our greatest geologists have maintained the immutability of species. But Sir Charles Lyell now gives the support of his high authority to the opposite side; and most geologists and palaeontologists are much shaken in their belief. For my part, I look at the geological record as a history of the world imperfectly kept, and written in a changing dialect; we possess the last volume alone, relating only to two or three countries. Of this volume, only here and there a short chapter has been preserved; and of each page, only here and there a few lines. Each word of the slowly-changing language may represent the forms of life, which falsely appear to have been abruptly introduced. On this view, the difficulties above discussed are greatly diminished, or even disappear.

CHAPTER XI

Geological Succession of Inorganic Beings

Species arise slowly, endure for unequal periods, and decline, through competition, even more slowly to extinction

New species have appeared very slowly, one after another. Lyell has shown that it is hardly possible to resist the evidence in the case of the several tertiary stages. In some recent beds only one or two species are extinct, and only one or two are new. The secondary formations are more broken; but, neither the appearance nor disappearance of the many species in each formation has been simultaneous.

Species belonging to different genera and classes have not changed at the same rate, or in the same degree. In the older tertiary beds a few living shells may still be found in the midst of extinct forms. Land productions seem to have changed at a quicker rate than those of the sea. Organisms high in the scale seem to change more quickly than those that are low: though there are exceptions. Yet if we compare any but the closest formations, all the species will have undergone some change. When a species has once disappeared from the earth, it never reappears. Genera and families follow the same rules.

These facts accord well with our theory. We can understand the apparently quicker rate of change in terrestrial and in more highly organised productions by their more complex relations to their conditions of life. We can understand from the all-important relations of organism to organism that any form which did not become improved would be liable to extermination. Hence we see why all species become modified, for otherwise they would become extinct.

Whole groups of species sometimes falsely appear to have been abruptly developed, but the general rule is a gradual increase until the group reaches its maximum. This is strictly conformable with the theory—one species first giving rise to two or three varieties, these being slowly converted into species, which in their turn produce other varieties and species, and so on.

On the theory of natural selection, the extinction of old forms and the production of improved forms are intimately connected. Species and groups of species gradually disappear, one after another, first from one spot, then from another, and finally from the world. Every creature is constantly being checked by unperceived hostile agencies amply sufficient to cause rarity, and finally extinction. So little is this subject understood, that I have heard surprise repeatedly expressed at monsters such as the Mastodon having become extinct; as if mere bodily strength gave victory in the battle of life. Insects and blood-sucking bats determine the existence of the larger naturalized quadrupeds in several parts of S. America.

Competition will generally be most severe between the forms which are most like each other. Improved descendants will generally cause the extermination of the parent-species; and if many new forms have been developed from any one species, the nearest allies will be the most liable to extermination. But a new species must often have seized on the place occupied by a species of a distinct group, and caused its extermination. A few sufferers may be preserved a long time, from being fitted to some peculiar line of life, or from inhabiting some isolated station and escaping severe competition. For instance, some species of Trigonia, a great genus of shells in the secondary formations, survive in the Australian seas. Utter extinction is generally a slower process than production.

Deposits at distant points of the world reveal that marine forms have changed simultaneously and in the same order

Scarcely any palaeontological discovery is more striking than the fact that the forms of life change almost simultaneously throughout the world. Thus our European Chalk formation can be recognised in many distant regions, where not a fragment of chalk can be found, from an unmistakeable resemblance in the organic remains. In some cases not one species is identically the same, but they belong to the same families, genera, and sections of genera. Moreover, forms which occur in the formations either above or below, occur in the same order. These observations, however, relate to the marine inhabitants of the world: we have not sufficient data, and may indeed doubt, whether the productions of the land and of fresh water at distant points change in the same parallel manner.

This great fact of parallel succession is explicable on the theory of natural selection. Forms which are already dominant give birth to the greatest number of new varieties or incipient species. We have distinct evidence on this head. It is also natural that the dominant, varying and far-spreading species would have the best chance of spreading still further and of giving rise in new countries to other species. The process of diffusion would often be very slow, but, in general, the dominant forms would ultimately prevail. Diffusion would be slower with the inhabitants of distinct continents. We might therefore expect to find, as we do find, less parallelism in land productions than with those of the sea. The old forms which are beaten will generally be allied in groups, from inheriting some inferiority in common; and therefore, the succession of forms everywhere tends to correspond also in final dissappearance.

I have given my reasons for believing that most of our great fossiliferous formations were deposited during periods of subsidence. During long blank intervals, a considerable amount of modifications, extinction, and migration occurred. But we are far from having any right to conclude that large areas have invariably been affected by the same movements. When two formations have been deposited in two regions during nearly, but not exactly, the same period, we should find in both the same general succession in the forms of life; but the species would not exactly correspond; for there will have been a little more time in one region than in the other for modification, extinction, and immigration. Thus, Mr. Prestwich, in his admirable Memoirs on the Eocene deposits of England and France, draws a close general parallel between the successive stages in the two countries; but although he finds accordance in the numbers of the species belonging to the same genera, the species themselves differ in a manner difficult to account for considering the proximity of the two areas.

Descent with modification explains the fact that extinct forms fill out intervals between existing forms, and between other fossils

All species fall into a few grand classes; and this fact is at once explained on the principle of descent. Extinct species can all be classed either in still existing groups, or between them. That extinct forms help to fill up the intervals between existing genera, families, and orders, is certainly true; but as this has often been ignored or denied, it may be well to give some instances. Cuvier ranked the Ruminants and Pachyderms as two of the most distinct orders of mammals: but so many fossil links have been disentombed that Owen has had to alter the whole classification; for example, he dissolves by gradations the wide interval between the pig and the camel. Even the wide interval between birds and reptiles has been shown by Professor Huxley to be partially bridged in the most unexpected manner, on the one hand, by the ostrich and extinct Archeopteryx, and on the other hand, by one of the dinosaurians—that group which includes the most gigantic of all terrestrial reptiles.

On the principle of the continued tendency to divergence we can understand the rule that the most ancient fossils differ most from existing forms. We must not, however, assume that divergence is necessary; it depends solely on the descendants being thus enabled to seize on different places in the economy of nature. A species might retain through a vast period the same general characteristics. All we have a right to expect is, that those groups which have, within known geological periods, undergone much modification, should in the older formations make some slight approach to each other; and this by the concurrent evidence of our best palaeontologists is frequently the case.

It is no real objection to the truth that the fauna of each period as a whole is nearly intermediate in character between preceding and succeeding faunas, that certain genera offer exceptions. For instance, the parent-rock-pigeon still lives and many varieties between the rock-pigeon and the carrier have become extinct. Closely connected with this truth is the fact that fossils from two consecutive formations are far more closely related to each other than are fossils from two remote formations. On the theory of descent, the full meaning of the fossil remains from closely consecutive formations being closely related is obvious. We find, in short, such evidence of the slow and scarcely sensible mutations of specific forms as we have the right to expect.

Natural selection accounts for the higher development of present forms over ancient, and for the parallel between geological succession and embryological development

The degree of differentiation of the parts in organic beings, when arrived at maturity, is the best standard as yet suggested of their degree of perfection. As specialisation is an advantage in the struggle for life, natural selection will tend to render each being more specialised. So that by the fundamental test of victory, modern forms ought, on the theory of natural selection, to stand higher than ancient forms. Is this the case? A large majority of palaeontologists would answer in the affirmative. The geological record, at all times imperfect, does not extend far enough back, to show unmistakeably that within the known history of the world organisation has largely advanced. To attempt to compare members of distinct types in the scale of highness seems hopeless; who will decide whether a cuttle-fish be higher than a bee? We ought not solely to compare the highest members of a class at any two periods, but all members, high and low, at the two periods. We ought also to compare the proportional numbers at any two periods of the high and low classes throughout the world: if, for instance, at the present day fifty thousand kinds of vertebrate animals exist and if we knew that at some former period only ten thousand existed, we ought to look at this increase in number in the highest class, which implies a great displacement of lower forms, as a decided advance. We thus see how hopelessly difficult it is to compare the imperfectly-known faunas of successive periods.

Agassiz and several other highly competent judges insist that the geological succession of extinct forms is nearly parallel with the embryological development of existing forms. This view accords admirably with our theory. Thus the embryo comes to be left as a sort of picture preserved by nature, of the former and less modified condition of the species. This may be true, and yet never capable of proof. For instance, the oldest known mammals, reptiles, and fishes strictly belong to their proper classes; it would be vain to look for animals having the common embryological character of the Vertebrata, until fossil beds are discovered far beneath the lowest Cambrian strata—a discovery of which the chance is small.

Living forms are closely allied to fossils in the same area

Mr. Clift many years ago showed that the fossil mammals from the Australian caves were closely allied to the living Australian marsupials. Professor Owen has shown in the most striking manner that most of the numerous fossil mammals of South America are related to living South American types, and has subsequently extended the same generalisation to the mammals of the Old World. Now what does this remarkable law of the succession of the same types within the same areas mean? He would be a bold man who, after comparing climates, would attempt to account through physical conditions for the similarity or dissimilarity of the inhabitants. On the theory of descent with modification, the great law of the long enduring but not immutable succession of the same types within the same areas is at once explained; for the inhabitants will obviously tend to leave in that quarter closely allied though in some degree modified descendants. If the inhabitants of one continent formerly differed greatly from those of another continent, so will their modified descendants still differ. But after long intervals of time and great geographical changes, permitting much intermigration, the feebler will yield to the more dominant forms, and there will be nothing immutable in the distribution of organic beings.

CHAPTER XII

Geological Distribution

Common ancestry accounts for the similarities—natural barriers and divergents through selection for the differences—of organic beings distributed over the globe

Notwithstanding the general parallelism in the conditions of the Old and New Worlds, how widely different are their living productions! If we compare large tracts of land in Australia, South Africa, and western South America, between latitudes 25° and 35°, we shall find parts extremely similar in all their conditions, yet it would not be possible to point out three faunas and floras more utterly dissimilar.

Barriers of any kind or obstacles to free migration are related in a close and important manner to the differences between the productions of various regions. We see this in the New and Old Worlds, excepting in the northern parts, where the land almost joins, and where, under a slightly different climate, there might have been free migration for the northern temperate forms, as there now is for the strictly arctic. On each continent, on the opposite sides of lofty mountain-ranges, of great deserts and even of large rivers, we find different productions; though as mountain-chains, deserts, etc., are not as impassable or likely to have endured so long as oceans, the differences are very inferior in degree to those characteristic of distinct continents.

Turning to the seas, we find the same law. The marine inhabitants of the eastern and western shores of South

America are very distinct. We meet in the eastern islands of the Pacific with a totally distinct fauna.

A third great fact is the affinity of the productions of the same continent or sea. The naturalist travelling from north to south hears from closely allied yet distinct kinds of birds notes nearly similar, and sees their nests similarly constructed, but not quite alike, with eggs coloured in nearly the same manner. The plains near the Straits of Magellan are inhabited by one species of American ostrich, the plains of La Plata by another species; and not by a true ostrich or emu, like those inhabiting Africa and Australia under the same latitude.

The bond is simply inheritance. The dissimilarity of the inhabitants of different regions may be attributed to modification through variation and natural selection, and probably in a subordinate degree to different physical conditions. The degrees of dissimilarity will depend on the migration of the more dominant forms having been more or less effectually prevented, at periods more or less remote; on the nature and number of the former immigrants; and on the action of the inhabitants on each other, the relation of organism to organism in the struggle for life being the most important of all relations.

As some forms have retained nearly the same character from an enormously remote geological period, so certain species have migrated over vast spaces, and have not become greatly or at all modified.

Species of the same genus, though inhabiting the most distant quarters of the world, must originally have proceeded from the same source, as they are descended from the same progenitor. In the case of those species which have undergone during whole geological periods little modification, there is not much difficulty in believing that they have migrated from the same region; for during the vast geographical and climatal changes which have supervened since ancient times, almost any amount of migration is possible. But in many other cases, in which the species of a genus have been produced within comparatively recent times, there is great difficulty.

The above principles, with their corollary—the origination of a species in one place —can explain the present distribution of plants and animals

We are thus brought to the question whether species have been created at one or more points of the earth's surface. The simplicity of the view that each species was first produced within a single region captivates the mind. He who rejects it, rejects the *vera causa* of ordinary generation with subsequent migration, and calls in the agency of miracle. In most cases the area inhabited by a species is continuous. The incapacity of migrating across a wide sea is more clear in the case of terrestrial mammals than with other organic beings; accordingly, we find no inexplicable instances of the same mammals inhabiting distant points of the world. But if the same species can be produced at separate points, why do we not find a single mammal common to Europe and Australia or South America? The conditions of life are the same, and some of the aboriginal plants are identical at distant points of the northern and southern hemispheres. The answer, I believe, is that mammals have not been able to migrate, whereas some plants, from their varied means of dispersal, have migrated across the wide and broken interspaces. Some few families, many sub-families, very many genera, and a greater number of sections of genera are confined to a single region. What a strange anomaly it would be if an opposite rule prevailed when we go down one step to the individuals of one species, and these had not been, at first, confined to some one region!

The geographical and climatal changes which have occurred within recent geological times must have rendered discontinuous the formerly continuous range of many species. So that we are reduced to consider whether the exceptions to continuity are so grave that we ought to give up the belief that each species has been produced within one area and migrated thence. No explanation can be offered of many instances. But if the existence of the same species at distant and isolated points can in many instances be explained, then, considering our ignorance of former climatal and geographical changes and of the various occasional means of transport, the belief that a single birthplace is the law, seems to me incomparably the safest.

This question differs from an allied question—whether all individuals of a species are descended from a single pair, or from many individuals simultaneously created. In the great majority of cases, with all organisms which unite for each birth or occasionally intercross, the individuals inhabiting the same area will be kept nearly uniform by intercrossing; so that many individuals will go on simultaneously changing, and the modification at each stage will not be due to descent from a single parent.

Changes of climate and geography, as well as many means of transport, explain identical species of plants in widely separated areas

Before discussing the three classes of facts which present the greatest difficulty on the theory of "single centres of creation," I must say a few words on the means of dispersal. Change of climate must have had a powerful influence on migration. A region now impassable might have been a high road when the climate was different. Changes of level in the land must also have been highly influential: a narrow isthmus now separates two marine faunas; let it formerly have been submerged, and the two faunas will have blended. Land may formerly have connected islands or possibly even continents, though I do not believe that within the recent period most of our continents have been united with each other and with existing oceanic islands. Several facts in the distribution are opposed to the admission of such prodigious recent geographical revolutions.

I must say a few words on occasional means of distribution. I shall confine myself to plants. Until I tried a few experiments, it was not even known how far seeds could resist the action of sea-water. To my surprise I found that out of 87 kinds, 64 germinated after an immersion of 28 days, and a few survived an immersion of 137 days. Certain orders were far more injured than others. I chiefly tried small seeds without the capsule or fruit; and as all of these sank in a few days they could not have been floated across wide spaces of the sea, whether or not they were injured by the salt-water. Afterwards I tried some larger fruits, capsules, etc., and some of these floated for a long time. The difference in the buoyancy of green and seasoned timber is well known. Hence I dried stems and branches of 94 plants with ripe fruit, and placed them on sea-water: hazel-nuts sank immediately, but when dried they floated for 90 days, and afterwards germinated; an asparagus-plant with ripe berries floated for 23 days; when dried it floated for 85, and the seeds germinated. Altogether, out of 94 dried plants, 18 floated for above 28 days. The average rate of the several Atlantic currents is 33 miles per diem. Thus, seeds might be floated across 924 miles of sea to another country, and when stranded, if blown by an inland gale to a favourable spot, would germinate.

Seeds may be occasionally transported in another manner. The natives of the coral-islands in the Pacific procure stones for their tools solely from the roots of drifted trees, these stones being a valuable royal tax. When stones are embedded in the roots of trees, small parcels of earth are frequently enclosed so perfectly that not a particle could be washed away during the longest transport: out of one small portion of earth thus *completely* enclosed, three plants germinated. Carcasses of birds, floating on the sea, sometimes escape being devoured; and many kinds of seeds in their crops long retain their vitality. Some from the crop of a pigeon, which had floated on artificial sea-water for 30 days, to my surprise nearly all germinated.

Living birds are highly effective in transporting seeds. Birds are blown by gales to vast distances across the ocean. Hard seeds of fruit pass uninjured through even the digestive organs of a turkey. But the following fact is more important: the crops of birds do not injure the germination of seeds. After a bird has devoured a large supply of food, all the grains do not pass into the gizzard for twelve or eighteen hours. A bird in this interval might easily be blown 500 miles; hawks are known to look out for tired birds, and the contents of their torn crops might thus readily get scattered. Some hawks and owls bolt their prey whole, and, after an interval of from twelve to twenty hours, disgorge pellets which include seeds capable of germination. Some seeds germinated after twelve to twenty-one hours in the stomachs of birds of prey. Fresh-water fish eat seeds of many land and water plants; fish are frequently devoured by birds and thus the seeds might be transported. Locusts are sometimes blown to great distances: A swarm might readily be the means of introducing plants into an island far from the mainland.

Although the beaks and feet of birds are generally clean, earth sometimes adheres to them. Prof. Newton sent me the leg of a partridge with a ball of hard earth adhering to it, weighing six and a half ounces. The earth had been kept for three years, but no less than 82 plants sprung from it: can we doubt that the many birds which are annually blown by gales across great spaces of ocean, and which annually migrate, must thus occasionally transport a few seeds?

As icebergs are known to be sometimes loaded with earth and stones, they must occasionally have transported seeds in the arctic and antarctic regions, and during the Glacial period in the now temperate regions.

Considering that these means of transport and others which remain to be discovered have been in action for tens of thousands of years, it would be a marvellous fact if many plants had not thus become widely transported. These means, however, would not suffice for occasional transport from one distant continent to another. Almost every year, one or two land-birds are blown across the Atlantic, but seeds could be transported by these rare wanderers only. And how small would be the chance of a seed falling on favourable soil, and coming to maturity! But it would be a great error to argue that a poorly-stocked island, though more remote from the mainland, would not receive colonists by similar means. On almost bare land, with few destructive insects or birds, nearly every seed which arrived, if fitted for the climate, would germinate and survive.

The slow alternation of warm and cold climates in the northern and southern hemispheres explains the movement of plant-species from north to south and from south to north

The identity of many plants and animals on mountain-summits, separated from each other by hundreds of miles of lowlands where Alpine species could not possibly exist, is one of the most striking cases of the same species living at distant points. The plants on the White Mountains in the United States are the same with those of Labrador, and nearly the same with those on the loftiest mountains of Europe. The Glacial period affords a simple explanation. We have evidence of almost every conceivable kind that, within a recent geological period, central Europe and North America suffered under an arctic climate. As the cold came on and as each more southern zone became fitted for the inhabitants of the north, these would take the places of the former inhabitants. The latter, at the same time, would travel further and further southward, unless stopped by barriers, in which case they would perish. The mountains would become covered with snow and ice and their Alpine inhabitants would descend to the plains. By the time that the cold had reached its maximum, we should have an arctic fauna and flora, nearly the same, covering central Europe and the now temperate regions of the United States; for the present circumpolar inhabitants, which everywhere travelled southward, are remarkably uniform around the world.

As the warmth returned, the arctic forms would retreat northward, closely followed up by the temperate forms. As snow melted from the mountains, the arctic forms would seize on the thawed ground, always ascending as the warmth increased and the snow further disappeared, whilst their brethren pursued their northern journey. Hence, when the warmth had returned, the same species which had lately lived together on the European and North American lowlands would again be found in arctic regions and on many isolated mountain-summits far distant from each other.

We can thus also understand that the Alpine plants of each mountain-range are more especially related to the arctic forms living north of them: for the migration would have been due south and north. Alpine plants, for example, of the Pyrenees are especially allied to the plants of northern Scandinavia, and those of the United States to Labrador.

As the arctic forms moved with the changing climate and all in a body together, they will not have been liable to much modification. But the Alpine productions left on the summits of mountains will have been far distant from each other; they will also probably have become mingled with ancient Alpine species temporarily driven down to the plains, and will have been subsequently exposed to different climatal influences. And they have been modified; for, though many of the species remain the same, some exist as varieties, some as sub-species, and some as distinct yet closely allied species representing each other on the several ranges.

But some of the species which now exist on the lower mountain-slopes and on the plains of North America and Europe are the same. During the Glacial period, when the inhabitants of the Old and New Worlds lived farther southwards, they must have been still more completely separated from each other by wider spaces of ocean; so that it may well be asked how the same species could then or previously have entered the two continents. The explanation lies in the climate before the Glacial period. At this period, the majority of the inhabitants of the world were the same as now, and we have good reason to believe the climate was warmer. Hence we may suppose that the organisms which now live under latitude 60° lived during the Pliocene farther north under the Polar Circle in latitude 66°—67°, where is almost continuous land from western Europe through Siberia to eastern America. And this will account for the uniformity of productions of the Old and New Worlds, at a period anterior to the Glacial epoch.

I am strongly inclined to extend the above view, and to infer, that during some still earlier and still warmer period, a large number of the same plants and animals inhabited the almost continuous circumpolar land and began slowly to migrate southwards as the climate became less warm, long before the commencement of the Glacial period. On this view we can understand the relationship with very little identity, between the productions of North America and Europe. We can further understand the singular fact that the productions of Europe and America during the later tertiary stages were more closely related to each other than they are now. As plants and animals migrated southward, they will have become mingled with native productions, and would have had to compete with them—and so be modified. Hence, with the now living productions of the temperate regions of the New and Old Worlds, we find few identical species, but in every class many forms which some naturalists rank as geographical races and others as distinct species, and a host of forms ranked by all naturalists as specifically distinct.

As on the land, so in the water a slow southern migration will account for many allied forms now living in marine areas completely sundered.

Mr. Croll has attempted to show that a glacial climate is the result of causes brought into operation by an increase in the eccentricity of the earth's orbit. Cold periods recur every ten or fifteen thousand years; and at long intervals they are extremely severe. When the northern hemisphere passes through a cold period the temperature of the southern hemisphere is actually raised, with the winters much milder, chiefly through changes in the direction of the ocean-currents, and so conversely with the northern hemisphere. This conclusion throws so much light on geographical distribution that I am strongly inclined to trust in it; but I will first give the facts.

Certain plants growing on the more lofty mountains of the tropics in all parts of the world and on the temperate plains of the north and south are either the same species or varieties of the same species. These plants are not strictly arctic forms. A list of the genera of plants collected on the loftier peaks of Java raises a picture of a collection made on a hillock in Europe! It appears almost certain that during the most severe part of a Glacial period, the lowlands of these great continents were everywhere tenanted under the equator by a considerable number of temperate forms, mingled with tropical vegetation, like those on the lower slopes of the Himalaya. Certainly some of the more vigorous and widest-spreading temperate forms invaded the equatorial lowlands. The southern hemisphere was at this period warmer. On the decline of the Glacial period, the northern temperate forms would have been driven to their former homes or have been destroyed, being replaced by the equatorial forms returning from the south. Some, however, would almost certainly have ascended any adjoining high land. They might have survived, even if the climate was not perfectly fitted for them, for the change of temperature must have been very slow, and plants possess a certain capacity for acclimatisation.

The southern hemisphere would in its turn be subjected to a severe Glacial period, with the northern hemisphere rendered warmer; and then the southern temperate forms would invade the equatorial lowlands. The northern forms which had before been left on the mountains would now descend and mingle with the southern forms. These latter, when the warmth returned, would return to their former homes, leaving some few species on the mountains, and carrying southward some of the northern temperate forms which had descended from their mountain fastnesses. Thus, we should have some few identical species in both temperate zones and on the mountains of the tropical regions. But the species left a long time on these mountains, or in opposite hemispheres, would be eminently liable to modification, and would generally now exist as varieties or as representative species; and this is the case.

Many more species have migrated from north to south than in reverse. I suspect this preponderance is due to the greater extent of land in the north, and to northern forms having consequently been advanced through competition to a higher stage than southern. In the same manner many European productions now cover the ground in La Plata, New Zealand, and to a lesser degree in Australia, and have beaten the natives; whereas extremely few southern forms have become naturalized in the northern hemisphere.

The same principles apply to the distribution of terrestrial animals and marine productions in both temperate zones, and the intertropical mountains.

Various difficulties remain to be solved. Some species are so distinct that there has not been time since the last

Glacial period for their modification to the necessary degree. I am inclined to look to a former and warmer period, when the Antarctic lands supported a highly peculiar and isolated flora. Before extermination a few forms may have been widely dispersed by occasional means of transport and by the aid, as halting-places, of now sunken islands.

CHAPTER XIII

Geological Distribution—Continued

Fresh water organisms are widely distributed by birds, floods and changes of water courses

As lakes and river-systems are separated from each other, it might have been thought that fresh-water productions would not have ranged widely within the same country, and as the sea is a still more formidable barrier, that they would never have extended to distant countries. But allied fresh-water species prevail in a remarkable manner throughout the world. Most cases can be explained by their having become fitted for short and frequent migrations from pond to pond or from stream to stream within their own countries.

A most difficult case to explain is fish. They often range widely, and as if capriciously; for in two adjoining river-systems some of the species may be the same and some wholly different. They are occasionally transported by accidental means. Fish still alive are not rarely dropped at distant points by whirlwinds, and the ova retain their vitality for a considerable time after removal from the water. Their dispersal may, however, be mainly attributed to changes in the level of the land within the recent period, causing rivers to flow into each other. This also has occurred during floods.

Some species of fresh-water shells have very wide ranges, and allied species which on our theory must have proceeded from a single source, prevail throughout the world. Two facts throw some light on this subject. When ducks suddenly emerge from a pond covered with duck-weed, I have twice seen these little plants adhering to their backs; and in removing a little duck-weed from one aquarium to another I have unintentionally stocked the one with fresh-water shells from the other. But another agency is perhaps more effectual: I suspended the feet of a duck in an aquarium, where many ova were hatching; numbers of shells crawled on the feet, and clung to them so firmly that they could not be jarred off. These just-hatched molluscs survived on the duck's feet, in damp air, from twelve to twenty hours, and in this length of time a duck or heron might fly at least six or seven hundred miles.

It has long been known what enormous ranges many fresh-water plants and marsh species have. I think favourable means of dispersal explain this fact. I have mentioned that earth occasionally adheres to the feet and beaks of birds. Wading birds, which frequent the muddy edges of ponds, wander more than any other; they are occasionally found on the most remote islands of the ocean. I tried several little experiments and will give the most striking: I took from a little pond three tablespoonfuls of mud weighing, when dried, only 6 ¾ ounces; I kept it six months, pulling up and counting each plant as it grew. The plants were 537 in number. I believe it would be inexplicable if water-birds did not transport seeds to unstocked ponds and streams at very distant points.

The inhabitants of oceanic islands differ from those of neighboring islands and continents in proportion to the water barrier

The species which inhabit oceanic islands are few compared with those on equal continental areas. He who admits the creation of separate species will have to admit that a sufficient number of the best adapted plants and animals were not created for oceanic islands, for man has unintentionally stocked them far more perfectly than did nature. Although the species are few, the proportion of endemic kinds (those found nowhere else) is often extremely large. This might have been expected, for species arriving in the new and isolated district, and having to compete with new associates, would be eminently liable to modification. But it by no means follows that, because in an island nearly all the species of one class are peculiar, those of another are peculiar. The difference seems to depend partly on the unmodified species having immigrated in a body, and partly on the frequent arrival of unmodified immigrants with which the insular forms have intercrossed. The offspring of such crosses would certainly gain in vigour, so that even an occasional cross would certainly produce more effect than might have been anticipated.

Oceanic islands are sometimes deficient in animals of certain whole classes, and their places are occupied by other classes; thus in the Galapagos Islands reptiles, and in New Zealand gigantic wingless birds, take, or recently took, the place of mammals. Such differences are generally accounted for by supposed differences in physical conditions, but this explanation is not a little doubtful. Facility of immigration seems to have been fully as important.

The general absence of frogs, toads, and newts on many oceanic islands cannot be accounted for by physical conditions, for frogs have been introduced in Madeira, the Azores and Mauritius, and have multiplied so as to become a nuisance. As they are immediately killed by sea-water, there would be great difficulty in their transportal across the sea. But why, on the theory of creation, they should not have been created there, it would be difficult to explain.

I have not found a single instance of a terrestrial mammal (excluding domesticated animals) inhabiting an island situated above 300 miles from a continent or great continental island. But aerial mammals occur on almost every island. Why has the supposed creative force produced bats and no other mammals on remote islands? But bats can fly.

Another interesting relation exists between the depth of the seas separating islands and the affinity of their mammalian inhabitants. The Malay Archipelago is traversed by a space of deep ocean, and this separates two widely distinct mammalian faunas. On either side, the islands stand on a shallow bank; these are inhabited by the same or by closely allied quadrupeds. As modifications depend on the lapse of time, and as the islands separated by shallow channels are more likely to have been continuously united within a recent period, we understand the relation between the depth of the sea and the degree of affinity—a relation inexplicable on the theory of independent acts of creation.

The Galapagos Archipelago lies 500 and 600 miles from the shores of South America. The naturalist, looking at the inhabitants of these volcanic islands feels that he is standing on American land. Why should the species which are supposed to have been created in the Galapagos Archipelago, and nowhere else, bear so plainly the stamp of affinity to those created in America? In the conditions of life, in the geological nature of the islands, in their height and climate there is a considerable dissimilarity from the South American coast. On the other hand, there is considerable resemblance between the Galapagos and Cape Verde Archipelagoes; but the inhabitants of the Cape Verde Islands are related to those of Africa. Such facts admit of no explanation on the view of independent creation. The endemic productions of islands are almost invariably related to those of the nearest continent or large island.

The same law is sometimes displayed within the limits of the same Archipelago. Thus each separate island of the Galapagos Archipelago is tenanted, and the fact is a marvellous one, by many distinct species; but these are related to each other in a much closer manner than to the inhabitants of the American continent. How is it that immigrants have been differently modified, though only in a small degree, in islands situated within sight of each other, having the same height, climate, etc.? The difficulty arises in chief part from the deeply-seated error of considering physical conditions as most important; whereas the nature of the species with which each has to compete is generally far more important. A plant, for instance, would find the ground best fitted for it occupied by somewhat different species in the different islands, and would be exposed to somewhat different enemies. If it varied, natural selection would probably favour different varieties in the different islands. The surprising fact is that each new species formed in any one island did not spread quickly to the others. Some of the species have spread, but we often take an erroneous view of the probability of closely-allied species invading each other's territory. If both are equally well fitted for their own places, both will probably hold their separate places for almost any length of time. Thus there are three closely-allied species of mocking-thrush, each confined to its own island. Suppose the mocking-thrush of Chatham Island to be blown to Charles Island; why should it succeed in establishing itself there? Charles Island is well stocked with its own species and the mocking-thrush of Charles Island is well fitted for its home. On the same continent, also, pre-occupation has probably played an important part in checking commingling. So it is with butterflies and other animals inhabiting the great open and continuous valley of the Amazon.

The relation to the source whence colonists could have been most easily derived, together with their subsequent modification, is of the widest application. We see this on every mountain-summit, in every lake and marsh. Wherever in two regions, however distant, many closely allied or representative species occur, there will be found some identical species, many forms which some naturalists rank as distinct species, and others as varieties, these doubtful forms showing us the steps in the progress of modification.

Lower organisms are more widely distributed than higher

The relation between the power and extent of migration in certain species, and the existence at remote points of the world of closely-allied species, is shown in a more general way. Within each class lower organisms change at a slower rate than higher; consequently they will have had a better chance of ranging widely and still retaining the same specific character. This fact, together with that of the seeds and eggs of most lowly organisms being very minute and better fitted for distant transportal, probably accounts for a law long observed, that the lower any group of organisms, the more widely it ranges.

CHAPTER XIV

Mutual Affinities of Organic Beings; Morphology; Embryology; Rudimentary Organs

Community of descent, the only valid basis for classification, is most manifest in characters which selection has not modified

From the most remote period organic beings have resembled each other in descending degrees, so that they can be classed in groups under groups. Within each country it is the widely ranging and dominant species, belonging to the larger genera in each class, which vary most. The varieties thus produced ultimately become converted into new species; and these, on the principle of inheritance, tend to produce other dominant species. Consequently large groups tend to go on increasing in size. From the descendants of each species trying to occupy as many and as different places as possible in the economy of nature, they constantly tend to diverge. Increasing forms exterminate the less divergent and less improved, so that we have many species descended from a single progenitor grouped into genera; and the genera into sub-families, families, and orders, all under one great class. The grand fact of the natural subordination of organic beings in groups under groups, from its familiarity, does not always sufficiently strike us.

Naturalists try to arrange each class on what is called the Natural System. But what is meant by this system? Some authors look at it merely as a scheme for arranging together those living objects which are most alike; or as an artificial method of enunciating, as briefly as possible, general propositions—that is, by one sentence to give the characters common, for instance, to all mammals, by another those common to all carnivora, by another those common to the dog-genus, and then, by adding a single sentence, a full description is given of each kind of dog. Expressions such as that famous one by Linnaeus that the characters do not make the genus, but that the genus gives the characters, seem to imply some deeper bond than mere resemblance. I believe that community of descent—the one known cause of close similarity in organic beings—is the bond.

It was thought in ancient times that those parts of the structure which determined habits of life were of high importance in classification. Nothing can be more false. No one regards the external similarity of a whale to a fish as of any importance. These resemblances are "adaptive or analogical." The less any part is concerned with special habits, the more important it becomes for classification. Owen says, "The generative organs, being most remotely related to the habits and food of an animal, I have always regarded as affording clear indications of its true affinities." Characters not functionally important are often constant throughout many allied groups, for natural selection acts only on serviceable characters. Rudimentary or atrophied organs are often of much value. The rudimentary teeth in the upper jaws of young ruminants and certain rudimentary bones of the leg are highly serviceable in exhibiting the close affinity between ruminants and pachyderms. Also, a classification founded on any single character, however important, has always failed; for no part is constant. The importance of an aggregate of characters, even when none are important, seems founded on many points of resemblance, too slight to be defined.

Practically, naturalists do not trouble themselves about physiological value. If they find a character nearly uniform, and common to a great number of forms, and not common to others, they use it as one of high value. If several trifling characters are always found in combination, though no apparent connection can be discovered between them, especial value is set on them. As important organs such as those for propelling the blood are nearly uniform, they are highly serviceable in classification, but in some groups vital organs offer characters of quite subordinate value. In the same group of crustaceans, Cypridina is furnished with a heart, whilst two closely allied genera have none. Embryonic, excluding larval, characters are of the highest value. The main divisions of flowering plants are founded on differences in the embryo.

Our classifications are often plainly influenced by chains of affinities. There are crustaceans at the opposite ends of series which have hardly a character in common; yet the species at both ends, from being plainly allied to others and so onwards, can be recognized as unequivocally belonging to this and to no other class. Geographical distribution has often been used, though perhaps not quite logically, in classification.

Finally, orders, families, sub-families, and genera seem to be, at least at present, almost arbitrary. A group first ranked by practised naturalists as only a genus has been raised to the rank of a sub-family or family, not because further research has detected important structural differences, but because numerous allied species with slightly different grades of difference, have been subsequently discovered.

All the foregoing rules and aids and difficulties may be explained on the view that the Natural System is founded on descent with modification.

The *arrangement* of the groups, in subordination and relation to each other, must be strictly genealogical in order to be natural; but the *amount* of difference in the several branches, though allied in the same degree in blood to their common progenitor, may vary greatly, due to the different degrees of modification which they have undergone; and this is expressed by the forms being ranked under different genera, families, sections, or orders.

With species in a state of nature, every naturalist has in fact brought descent into his classification; for he includes the two sexes; and he includes monsters and varieties, not from their partial resemblance to the parentform, but because they are descended from it. May not this element of descent have been unconsciously used by naturalists in classification? As we have no pedigrees, we are forced to trace community of descent by resemblances of any kind. Therefore we choose those characters which are the least likely to have been modified.

Similar adaptations in different orders are valueless in classification, for external resemblance only conceals essential difference

We can understand, on the above views, the important distinction between real affinities and analogical or adaptive resemblances. Animals of two distinct lines of descent may have become adapted to similar conditions and thus have assumed a close external resemblance. The shape of the body and fin-like limbs are only analogical when whales are compared with fish, being adaptations in both classes for swimming; but between the several members of the whale family, these parts exhibit true affinity; for as they are so nearly similar throughout the whole family, we cannot doubt that they have been inherited from a common ancestor. The extraordinary cases of widely different fish possessing electric organs—of widely different insects possessing luminous organs—come under this same head of analogical resemblances. The end gained is the same, but the means, though appearing superficially to be the same, are essentially different.

In another curious class of cases resemblance does not depend on adaptations to similar habits of life, but has been gained for the sake of protection. Butterflies imitate other and quite distinct species; the counterfeiters have changed their dress and externally do not resemble their nearest allies. Why has nature condescended to the tricks of the stage? The mocked forms always abound in numbers, and are distasteful to birds and other insect-devouring animals. The mocking forms are comparatively rare; hence they must suffer habitually from some danger. A member of one of these rare groups first varies; when a variety happens to resemble in some degree any little-persecuted butterfly, this variety has a better chance of escaping destruction; "the less perfect resemblances being generation after generation eliminated, and only the others left to propagate their kind." Here we have an excellent illustration of natural selection.

Aberrant forms are intermediate survivors of the extinction which has confined all organisms into very few classes

Dominant species tend to inherit the advantages which made the groups to which they belong large. They are almost sure to spread widely and seize on more and more places in the economy of nature. Thus we can account for the fact that all organisms, recent and extinct, are included under a few great orders, and under still fewer classes. The discovery of Australia has not added an insect belonging to a new class; and in the vegetable kingdom it has added only two or three families of small size.

I attempted to show why the more ancient forms of life are often in some degree intermediate between existing groups. As some few intermediate forms have transmitted to the present day descendants but little modified, these constitute our so-called osculant or aberrant species. The more aberrant any form is, the greater must be the number of connecting forms which have been lost. We can, I think, account for aberrant groups as forms which have been conquered by more successful competitors, with a few members still preserved under unusually favourable conditions.

Affinity of an organism to a group not its own is general, showing ancient community of descent

When a member belonging to one group of animals exhibits an affinity to a quite distinct group, this affinity in most cases is general and not special; thus, of all Rodents, the bizcacha is most nearly related to Marsupials; but in the points in which it approaches this order, its relations are general, that is, not to any one marsupial species more than to another. Either all Rodents branched off from some ancient Marsupial, or both Rodents and Marsupials branched off from a common progenitor. But the bizcacha retained more of the characters of its ancient progenitor than have other Rodents; and therefore will not be specially related to any one existing Marsupial, but indirectly to all or nearly all Marsupials.

Extinction has played an important part in defining and widening the intervals between groups. Many ancient forms have been lost, through which the early progenitors of birds were formerly connected with the early progenitors of the other and at that time less differentiated vertebrate classes. There has been less extinction within some whole classes: with the Crustacea, wonderfully diverse forms are still linked by a long and only partially broken chain of affinities.

Despite infinite diversity of adaptation, a fundamental similarity of structure remains unaltered in members of the same class

Members of the same class, independently of their habits of life, resemble each other in the general plan of their organization. This resemblance is often expressed by the term "unity of type"; or by saying that the several parts and organs are homologous. This subject is termed Morphology. This is one of the most interesting departments of natural history, and may almost be said to be its very soul. What can be more curious than that the hand of a man, formed for grasping, that of a mole for digging, the leg of the horse, the paddle of the porpoise, and the wing of the bat, should all be constructed on the same pattern, with similar bones, in the same relative positions?

The explanation is simple on the theory of the selection of slight modifications, often affecting by correlation other parts of the organisation. The bones of a limb might be shortened and flattened to any extent, becoming at the same time enveloped in thick membrane so as to serve as a fin; or a webbed hand might have its bones lengthened to any extent, with the membrane connecting them increased, so as to serve as wing; yet these modifications would not alter the framework of the bones or their relative connection. If we suppose that an early progenitor—the archetype of all mammals, birds, and reptiles—had its limbs constructed on the existing general pattern, we perceive the signification of the homologous construction of the limbs throughout the class. So with the mouths of insects, we have only to suppose that a common progenitor had an upper lip, mandibles, and two pairs of maxillae, and natural selection will account for the infinite diversity in the structure and functions of the mouths of insects.

Repetition of the same organ characterizes low forms; higher forms show originally identical organs adapted for extremely diverse uses

There is another and equally curious branch of our subject; namely, serial homologies, or the comparison of the different parts or organs in the same individual. The anterior and posterior limbs in all the higher vertebrae are plainly homologous. It is familiar to almost everyone that in a flower the relative position and intimate structure of the sepals, petals, stamens, and pistils are intelligible on the view that they consist of metamorphosed leaves, arranged in a spire. We can actually see, during the early or embryonic stages of development in flowers, as well as in crustaceans and many other animals, that organs, which when mature become extremely different, are at first exactly alike.

How inexplicable are serial homologies on the ordinary view of creation! Why should the brain be enclosed in a box composed of numerous and extraordinarily shaped pieces of bone, apparently representing vertebrae? Why should one crustacean, with a complex mouth formed of many parts, consequently always have fewer legs; or conversely, those with many legs have simpler mouths?

On the theory of natural selection, we can, to a certain extent, answer these questions. An indefinite repetition of the same part is characteristic of low or little specialised forms; therefore the unknown progenitor of the Vertebrata probably possessed many vertebrae; the unknown progenitor of the Articulata, many segments; and the unknown progenitor of the flowering plants, many leaves arranged in one or more spires. Parts many times repeated are eminently liable to vary in number and in form. Consequently such parts afford the materials for adaptation to the most different purposes, yet retain, through inheritance, plain traces of their fundamental resemblance.

In the early stages embryos of members of the same class are exceedingly similar The subject of development and embryology is one of the most important in natural history. The metamorphoses of insects are generally effected abruptly by a few stages; but the transformations are in reality numerous and gradual, though concealed. Changes during development, however, reach their acme in the so-called alternate generations of some of the lower animals. It is an astonishing fact that a delicate branching coralline attached to a submarine rock should produce, first by budding and then by division, a host of huge floating jelly-fishes; and that these should produce eggs from which are hatched swimming animalcules, which attach themselves to rocks and become developed into branching corallines; and so on in an endless cycle.

Generally embryos of the most distinct species belonging to the same class are closely similar, but become, when fully developed, widely dissimilar. A better proof of this cannot be given than the statement by Von Baer that "the embryos of mammalia, of birds, lizards, and snakes are in their earliest states so exceedingly like one another, that we can often distinguish the embryos only by their size. The feet of lizards and mammals, the wings and feet of birds, no less than the hands and feet of man all arise from the same fundamental form."

Adaptations appear when activity is required

The points of structure, in which the embryos resemble each other, often have no direct relation to their conditions of existence. For instance, in the embryos of the Vertebrata the peculiar loop-like courses of the arteries near the branchial slits cannot be related to similar conditions—in the young mammal which is nourished in the womb of its mother, in the egg of the bird which is hatched in a nest, and in the spawn of a frog under water.

The case is different when an animal during any part of its embryonic career has to provide for itself. Then the adaptation of the larva to its conditions is as beautiful as in the adult animal, so that the similarity of the larvae of allied animals is sometimes greatly obscured; especially when there is a division of labour during the different stages of development, as when the same larva has during one stage to search for food, and during another, for a place of attachment.

The embryo in the course of development generally rises in organisation. In some cases, however, the mature animal must be considered as lower in the scale than the larva. In some parasitic crustaceans, the larvae become developed into hermaphrodites having the ordinary structure, and into complemental males; and in the latter development is retrograde, for the male is a mere sack, short-lived and destitute of mouth, stomach, and every other organ of importance, excepting those for reproduction.

In some whole groups of animals, for instance spiders, the embryo never differs widely from the adult. Most insects pass through a worm-like stage, but in Aphis, for example, we see hardly any trace of this.

How can we explain these several facts in embryology?

It is commonly assumed that variations or individual differences appear at an early period. What evidence we have points the other way; breeders cannot positively tell, until some time after birth, what will be the merits or demerits of their young animals. We cannot tell whether a child will be tall or short, or what its precise features will be. The question is, at what period the effects are displayed. The cause may have acted on one or both parents before the act of generation. It is of no importance to an animal as long as it is nourished and protected by its parent, whether its characters are acquired a little earlier or later. It would not signify to a bird which obtained its food by having a much-curved beak whether it possessed a beak of this shape as long as it was fed by its parents.

At whatever period of maturity a variation occurs, it appears in the offspring at a corresponding, or an earlier, period

At whatever age a variation first appears in the parent, it tends to re-appear at a corresponding age in the offspring. These two principles, namely, that slight variations appear at a not very early period of life, and are inherited at a corresponding not early period, explain the leading facts in embryology.

As we have conclusive evidence that the breeds of the Pigeon are descended from a single wild species, I compared the young within twelve hours after being hatched; pouters, fantails, runts, barbs, dragons, carriers, and tumblers. Some of these, when mature, differ in so extraordinary a manner that they would have been ranked as distinct genera if found in a state of nature. But with the nestling birds the proportional differences were incomparably less than in the full-grown birds. Some characteristic points of difference could hardly be detected.

We may extend this view to widely distinct structures and to whole classes. Whatever influence long-continued use or disuse may have had in modifying any species, this will chiefly have affected it when nearly mature, when it was compelled to gain its own living. Thus the young will not be modified, or only slightly, through the effects of the use or disuse.

With some animals successive variations may have supervened at an early period, or may have been inherited at an earlier age than that at which they first occurred. Then the young or embryo will closely resemble the mature parent-form. This is the rule of development in certain whole groups, or sub-groups, as with cuttle-fish, land-shells, fresh-water crustaceans, spiders, and some insects. This would follow from the young having to provide at a very early age for their own wants, and from their following the same habits of life with their parents; for it would be indispensable for their existence that they should be modified in the same manner as their parents.

If, on the other hand, it profited the young to follow habits slightly different from those of the parent, on the principle of inheritance at corresponding ages, the young or the larvae might be rendered by natural selection more and more different from their parents, and differences in larva might become correlated with successive stages of its development; so that the larva, in the first stage might come to differ greatly from the larva in the second stage. The adult might also become fitted for sites or habits, in which organs of locomotion or of the senses would be useless; and in this case the metamorphosis would be retrograde. Most of our best authorities are now convinced that the various larval and pupal stages of insects have thus been acquired through adaptation, and not through inheritance from some ancient form.

Embryological and rudimentary parts, rendered useless by disuse, reveal ancestral adaptions through natural selection

On the other hand with many animals the embryonic or larval stages show us the condition of the progenitor of the whole group in its adult state. We can thus see why ancient and extinct forms so often resemble the embryos of existing species of the same class. So it is probable, from what we know of the embryos of mammals, birds, fishes, and reptiles, that these animals are the modified descendants of some ancient progenitor, which was furnished in its adult state with branchiae, a swim-bladder, four fin-like limbs, and a long tail, all fitted for an aquatic life.

The embryo is even more important for classification than the adult. If two or more groups of animals pass through closely similar embryonic stages, we may feel assured that they all are descended from one parent-form, and are closely related. But dissimilarity in embryonic development does not prove discommunity of descent, for in one of two groups the developmental stages may have been so greatly modified as to be no longer recognisable.

Embryology rises greatly in interest, when we look at the embryo as a picture, more or less obscured, of the progenitor, either in its adult or larval state, of all the members of the same great class.

Organs or parts which are rudimentary, atrophied, or aborted, bearing the plain stamp of inutility, are general throughout nature. In the mammalia, for instance, the males possess rudimentary mammae; in snakes one lobe of the lungs is rudimentary. What can be more curious than the presence of teeth in foetal whales, which when grown up have not a tooth in their heads?

Rudimentary organs plainly declare their origin and meaning in various ways. They sometimes retain their potentiality: as with the mammae of male mammals, which have been known to become well developed and to secrete milk. Various parts in a perfect state may in one sense be rudimentary, for they are useless. As Mr. G. H. Lewes remarks, "the Salamandra atra never lives in the water. Yet if we open a gravid female, we find tadpoles with exquisitely feathered gills, which swim like tadpoles of the water-newt. Obviously, this aquatic organisation has reference solely to ancestral adaptations; it repeats a phase in the development of its progenitors." Again, an organ may become rudimentary for its proper purpose, and be used for a distinct one; in certain fishes the swim-bladder seems to be rudimentary for its proper function of giving buoyancy, but has become converted into a nascent lung.

Rudimentary organs in the individuals of the same and closely allied species are liable to vary in the extent to which the same organ has been reduced. Organs which analogy would lead us to expect, and which are occasionally found in monstrous individuals, are utterly aborted in certain animals or plants. In tracing the homologies of any part in different members of the same class, nothing is more common, or, in order fully to understand the relations of the parts, more useful than the discovery of rudiments.

Rudimentary organs can often be detected in the embryo, but afterwards wholly disappear. Also, a rudimentary part is of greater relative size in the embryo so that the organ at this age cannot be said to be rudimentary. On the view of descent with modification we can understand to a large extent the laws governing their imperfect development. We learn from our domestic productions that the disuse of parts leads to their reduced size; and that the result is inherited. Disuse has probably been the main agent under nature, with the eyes of animals inhabiting dark caverns. Again, an organ might become injurious under certain conditions, as with the wings of beetles living on exposed islands; and in this case natural selection will have aided in reducing the organ until it was rendered harmless.

An organ rendered useless or injurious for one purpose, might be modified and used for another purpose. An organ might, also, be retained for one of its former functions. Organs when rendered useless may well be variable, for their variations can no longer be checked by natural selection. All this agrees with what we see under nature. Moreover, at whatever period of life either disuse or selection reduces an organ—generally at maturity—the principle of inheritance at corresponding ages will tend to reproduce the organ in its reduced state at the same mature age, but will seldom effect it in the embryo. Thus we can understand the greater size of rudimentary organs in embryo.

But after an organ has ceased being used and has become in consequence much reduced, how can it be finally quite obliterated? The principle of the economy of growth, by which the materials forming any part are saved as far as possible, will perhaps come into play. But a minute papilla, for instance, could not be absorbed for the sake of economising nutriment. Some additional explanation is here requisite which I cannot give.

CHAPTER XV

Conclusion

Descent with modification explains more facts about species than does any other theory
Nothing at first can appear more difficult to believe than that the more complex organs and instincts have been perfected, not by means superior to human reason, but by the accumulation of innumerable slight variations, each good for the individual possessor. I have felt these difficulties far too heavily during many years to doubt their weight. But the more important objections relate to questions on which we are confessedly ignorant; nor do we know how ignorant we are. Serious as they are, in my judgment they are by no means sufficient to overthrow the theory of descent with subsequent modification.

Now let us turn to the other side of the argument. Under domestication we see much variability, caused often in so obscure a manner that we are tempted to consider the variations as spontaneous. On the other hand, we have evidence that variability when it has once come into play never ceases. Under nature during the constant Struggle for Existence, we see a powerful and ever-acting form of Selection. A grain in the balance may determine which individuals shall live and which shall die. What limit can be put to this power, acting during long ages and rigidly scrutinising the whole constitution, structure, and habits of each creature? I can see no limit to this power, in slowly and beautifully adapting each form to the most complex relations of life. The theory of natural selection, even if we look no farther than this, seems to be in the highest degree probable.

If we admit that the geological record is extremely imperfect, then the facts which the record does give strongly support the theory. The grand fact that all extinct beings can be classed with all recent beings follows from the living and the extinct being the offspring of common parents. Lastly, the wonderful law of the long endurance of allied forms on the same continent is intelligible, for the existing and the extinct will be allied by descent.

Looking to geographical distribution, the existence of closely allied or representative species in any two areas implies that the same parent-forms formerly inhabited both areas; and we almost invariably find that some identical species are still common to both. The inhabitants of each area are related to the inhabitants of the nearest source whence immigrants might have been derived. These facts receive no explanation on the theory of creation.

How is it that organs bearing the plain stamp of inutility should so frequently occur? Nature may be said to have taken pains to reveal her scheme of modification by means of rudimentary organs, of embryological and homologous structures, but we are too blind to understand her meaning.

As my conclusions have been much misrepresented, and it has been stated that I attribute the modification of species exclusively to natural selection, I may remark that in the first edition of this work and subsequently, I placed in a most conspicuous position the following words: "I am convinced that natural selection has been the main but not the exclusive means of modification." This has been of no avail. Great is the power of steady misrepresentation; but the history of science shows that fortunately this power does not long endure.

It can hardly be supposed that a false theory would explain so satisfactorily the several large classes of facts above specified. It has been objected that this is an unsafe method of arguing; but it has often been used by the greatest natural philosophers. The undulatory theory of light has thus been arrived at; and the belief in the revolution of the earth on its own axis was until lately supported by hardly any direct evidence. It is no valid objection that science as yet throws no light on the far higher problem of the essence or origin of life. Who can explain what is the essence of the attraction of gravity? Yet no one now objects to following out the results consequent on this unknown element of attraction.

Until recently, people have been reluctant to accept evolution and natural selection

I see no good reason why the views given in this volume should shock religious feelings. The greatest discovery ever made by man, the law of gravity, was also attacked by Leibnitz, "as subversive of natural, and inferentially of revealed, religion." A celebrated author and divine has written to me that "he has gradually learnt to see that it is just as noble a conception of the Deity to believe that He created a few original forms capable of self-development into other and needful forms, as to believe that He required a fresh act of creation to supply the voids caused by the action of His laws."

Why until recently did nearly all eminent naturalists and geologists believe in the immutability of species? The belief was almost unavoidable as long as the history of the world was thought to be of short duration. It is so easy to hide our ignorance under such expressions as the "plan of creation," "unity of design," etc., and to think that we give an explanation when we only re-state a fact. A few naturalists, endowed with much flexibility of mind and who have already begun to doubt the immutability of species, may be influenced by this volume; but I look to the future—to young and rising naturalists, who will be able to view both sides of the question with impartiality. Whoever is led to believe that species are mutable will do good service by conscientiously expressing his conviction; for thus only can the load of prejudice be removed.

It may be maintained that all organisms are descended from a single primordial form

It may be asked how far I extend the doctrine of the modification of species. I believe that animals are descended from at most only four or five progenitors, and plants from an equal or lesser number. Analogy would lead me one step farther, to the belief that all animals and plants are descended from some one prototype. All living things have much in common in their chemical composition, their cellular structure, their laws of growth, and their liability to injurious influences. With all the germinal vesicle is the same; so that all organisms start from a common origin. If we look even to the two main divisions, the animal and vegetable kingdoms, certain low forms are so far intermediate that naturalists have disputed to which kingdom they should be referred. It does not seem incredible that, from such low and intermediate forms, both animals and plants may have been developed; and, if we admit this, we must likewise admit that all the organic beings may be descended from some one primordial form. But this inference is chiefly grounded on analogy and it is immaterial whether or not it be accepted.

The views expressed in this work will open up many fields of inquiry

When the views advanced by me in this volume, and by Mr. Wallace, or when analogous views on the origin of species are generally admitted, we can dimly foresee that there will be a considerable revolution in natural history. Systemists will not be incessantly haunted by the shadowy doubt whether this or that form be a true species. This, and I speak after experience, will be no slight relief. We shall be compelled to acknowledge that the only distinction between species and well-marked varieties is, that the latter are believed to be connected at the present day by intermediate gradations, whereas species ⟩ were formerly thus connected.

The other and more general departments of natural history will rise greatly in interest. When we no longer look at an organic being as a savage looks at a ship, as wholly beyond his comprehension; when we contemplate every complex structure and instinct as the summing up of many contrivances, in the same way as any great mechanical invention is the summing up of the labour, the experience, the reason, and even the blunders of numerous workmen—how far more interesting does the study of natural history become!

A grand and almost untrodden field of inquiry will be opened, on the causes and laws of variation, on correlation, on the effects of use and disuse, on the direct action of external conditions, and so forth. Psychology will be securely based on the foundation already well laid by Mr. Herbert Spencer, that of the necessary acquirement of each mental power and capacity by gradation. Much light will be thrown on the origin of man and his history.

The concept of descent with modification explains terrestrial life as long-enduring, collectively secure, and subjected by the Creator to unalterable law

To my mind it accords better with what we know of the laws impressed on matter by the Creator, that the production and extinction of the inhabitants of the world should have been due to secondary causes, like those determining the birth and death of the individual. When I view all beings not as special creations, but as the lineal descendants of some few beings which lived long before the first bed of the Cambrian system was deposited, they seem to me to become ennobled. Judging from the past, we may safely infer that not one living species will transmit its unaltered likeness to a distant futurity, and very few will transmit progeny of any kind. But we may feel certain that the succession by generation has never once been broken since long before the Cambrian epoch, and that no cataclysm has desolated the whole world. Hence we may look with some confidence to a secure future of great length. And as natural selection works solely by and for the good of each being, all corporeal and mental endowments will tend to progress towards perfection.

It is interesting to contemplate a tangled bank, clothed with many plants, with birds singing on the bushes, with insects flitting about, and with worms crawling through the damp earth, and to reflect that these elaborately constructed forms, dependent upon each other in so complex a manner, have all been produced by laws acting around us, these laws, taken in the largest sense, being Growth and Reproduction; Inheritance; Variability from the indirect and direct action of the conditions of life, and from use and disuse; a Ratio of Increase so high as to lead to a Struggle for Life, and as a consequence to Natural Selection, entailing Divergence of Character and Extinction of less-improved forms. Thus, from the war of nature, from famine and death, the most exalted object which we are capable of conceiving, namely, the production of higher animals, directly follows. There is grandeur in this view of life, with its several powers, having been originally breathed by the Creator into a few forms or into one; and that, whilst this planet has gone cycling on according to the fixed law of gravity, from so simple a beginning endless forms most beautiful and most wonderful have been, and are being evolved.